FROM LIFESAVING TO MARINE RESEARCH
STATION 119

KENNETH W. ABLE

FROM LIFESAVING TO MARINE RESEARCH
STATION 119

KENNETH W. ABLE

RUTGERS UNIVERSITY
MARINE FIELD STATION

DOWN THE SHORE
PUBLISHING
WEST CREEK N.J.

The words "Down The Shore" and the Down The Shore Publishing logo are registered U.S. Trademarks.

For information, address:
Down The Shore Publishing Corp., Box 100, West Creek, NJ 08092
www.down-the-shore.com

Printed in the United States of America on recycled paper, 10% post-consumer content.
10 9 8 7 6 5 4 3 2 1

Edited by Steve Warren
Book design by Leslee Ganss

Library of Congress Cataloging-in-Publication Data

Able, Kenneth W., 1945-
 Station 119 : from lifesaving to marine research / Kenneth W. Able.
  pages cm
 ISBN 978-1-59322-096-9 (pbk.)
1. Little Egg Coast Guard Station (N.J.)--History. 2. Lifesaving stations--New Jersey--Little Egg Harbor--History. 3. Rutgers University. Institute of Marine and Coastal Sciences--History. 4. Little Egg Harbor (N.J.)--Buildings, structures, etc. I. Title.
VK1324.N5A25 2015
551.46072'074948--dc23
           2015004703

*Sketch of a fiddler crab (*Uca pugnax*) with the field station in the background by Kenneth L. Gosner, author of* A Field Guide to the Atlantic Shore.

CONTENTS

INTRODUCTION

The history of the coastal rescue stations of the former U.S. Lifesaving Service and today's U.S. Coast Guard along New Jersey's shoreline is a very important part of the overall history of the state's development of coastal villages and towns in the 19th century. Many Americans do not realize that the very first federally established coastal shipwreck rescue facilities in the United States were established in New Jersey in 1849, and that from the perspective of shore-based rescue efforts, New Jersey is the birthplace of the U.S. Lifesaving Service, which became part of the U.S. Coast Guard in 1915.

Over the last half of the 1800s what was originally a barren and unsettled New Jersey coastline was gradually populated with the construction of manned life-saving stations approximately every four to five miles from Sandy Hook at the north to Cape May at the south. Each station was manned by a crew comprised of seven to ten surfmen and the station's keeper (or officer-in-charge). These stations and their surfman crews were responsible for conducting search and rescue operations in response to the ship-wrecks that were tragically occurring with regularity along the New Jersey shoreline. Many of these men were married and, while assigned to a particular station, would house their families in nearby shanties or cottages. In this manner, many of these stations served as the nucleus for the later establishment of many New Jersey shoreside villages and towns that today serve as destinations for seasonal beachgoers.

The stations and associated boats and rescue equipment were designed and constructed to withstand severe conditions of weather and use. Since its establishment in the nineteenth century up to present day, this system of stations, surfman crews, and boats and equipment has been directly responsible for saving thousands of lives from shipwrecks or boating accidents. Today's U.S. Coast Guard continues to carry on this humanitarian live-saving tradition, with a modernized but much reduced network of stations along the New Jersey coast and across the nation.

The former Little Egg Coast Guard Station, now the Rutgers University Marine Field Station (RUMFS), was an important part of the original system of stations along the New Jersey coastline and helped to guard what was at one time one of the most important entrance inlets in New Jersey for both commercial and recreational watercraft. Both at its original location on the now long-gone Tucker's Island, and later at its current location at the southeasterly end of Tuckerton Meadows, surfmen kept continuous watch over the inlet entrance for commercial shipping and recreational boats that might be wrecked or in danger.

National Archives

Although there were a number of different architectural station designs developed over the history of the U.S. Lifesaving Service and U.S. Coast Guard, the Colonial Revival type "Roosevelt" model developed as part of President Franklin D. Roosevelt's 1930s Depression era Work Projects Administration was one of the most attractive ever designed by the service. The former Little Egg station is one surviving example of this style of Coast Guard station architecture. Rutgers University's acquisition and restoration of this station definitely saved this historic complex of buildings from otherwise certain destruction. It is very fitting, therefore, that today as a marine sciences field station, the former Coast Guard station and its assigned faculty and student staff are keeping watch over and studying the region's precious natural marine resources, and helping to rescue those that are in danger of destruction or extinction.

Timothy R. Dring
Commander, U.S. Naval Reserve-Retired
President, U.S. Lifesaving Service Heritage Association

Coast Guard Station 119 at Little Egg Inlet with Coast Guard vessels tied up in the boat basin.

FOREWORD

This history of the station is clearly a labor of love for Dr. Ken Able. As a sometime scientist and historian practicing along this old New Jersey coast, I know how long it took to accumulate and synthesize the contents of this volume. Pieces are recovered in isolation and only after a long search and digestion do facts and anecdotes coalesce into something like a cohesive story.

Rutgers University, nationwide, was a cradle for many of the earliest marine scientists. Strangely, these began emerging from the Department of Agriculture with the arrival of Julius Nelson at the turn of the 20th century. He was creative enough to argue that oyster harvesting was a form of farming; generations ahead of the modern science of aquaculture, Nelson recognized that unregulated "harvest" of coastal shellfish populations depleted what the natural environment could replenish. Humans would have to look at being sustainable and people would have to work out how to replant what they took. This becomes a principle for society today; in fact, for the whole world.

Able's patient ferreting out of the articles and papers Julius wrote, and those his sons Thurlow (and to a lesser extent Richards Nelson) later contributed, required searching the Rutgers Agricultural Experiment Station literature rather than marine biological journals. It was only in the next generation that Thurlow's student H.H. "Hurricane Hal" Haskin began to break into the wider marine science literature. He became known world-wide for his sober judgment, based on long term data.

It was later still that students of Haskin and his Rutgers colleagues (both salt and freshwater biologists) began sending out educated people who have marked marine biology on an international scale: Perry H. Jeffries, Melbourne Carriker, David Flemer… the list goes on.

Rutgers was slow to recognize its own contributions; many of my own professors in the 1960s were frustrated by the lack of a cohesive marine program. As a burgeoning "marine ecologist" my own advanced degrees were from the Department of Botany! Furthermore my research was largely funded by business interests constructing a nuclear generating station on Barnegat Bay, not by any organization truly interested in advancing scientific knowledge. Rutgers Professor Michael Kennish came out of the same institutional frustration, leaving the private sector to pursue a clearer goal of environmental science.

In this volume, Able chronicles the awakening and wisdom of the university in developing a real marine science program, and its sensible long-term decision to make a research facility out of what was nearly the ruin of a disused and vandalized U.S. Coast Guard station. Its location is unique, at the juncture of estuary and sea, on one of the nation's last relatively pristine estuarine systems, the Mullica River. Able's story will lead you through the chain of people and intellects that made the station bear fruit.

Long term data are the key to understanding how our environments are changing — and often failing. It is the consistent, non-sexy discipline of monitoring our natural world that will provide a stable base for knowledge and good decision making. With support from Rutgers and from the wider world of research funding institutions, long may the old station and its works prosper.

Kent Mountford, PhD
Rutgers 1960, 1969 and 1971
Estuarine Ecologist and Environmental Historian

PREFACE
ONE MILLION AND COUNTING

On the evening of January 20, 2014, a sampling crew set out under a waning moon from the Rutgers University Marine Field Station (RUMFS) at the end of Great Bay Boulevard, armed with nets, flowmeters, buckets and a datalogger for measuring temperature and salinity. The mission was to collect larval fish. On the surface, this evening was nothing special. Station personnel have been performing pretty much the same task every week for the past twenty-five years as part of a sampling program to estimate the numbers and kinds of larvae being transported from their Atlantic Ocean spawning grounds to their estuarine nurseries.

On this evening the crew set their small mesh plankton nets from the bridge over Little Sheepshead Creek at about 8:00 p.m. The timing was planned. The tide had changed an hour earlier, and with it coming in quickly, the larvae could not see the nets and avoid capture. A half hour later, the first of three sets was retrieved. Part of the crew rushed back the mile or so of Great Bay Boulevard with the first sample and began sorting the fish larvae from the bits of plant material, jellyfish, shrimp, crabs and other crustaceans that had been swept up in the net.

What did make this evening special is this: Among the larvae collected, sorted, and preserved in vials was the millionth individual measured in the program's quarter century. It was a half-inch long summer flounder, a species that has received special attention over the years. Staff members took the small flounder and all the other larvae collected in that sample and packaged and stored them at the station's warehouse for continued study. Then, with no pause for celebration, the crew returned to the bridge for the next sample.

The Rutgers University Marine Field Station's southern New Jersey location is ideally located between two large ocean water masses, the Labrador Current from the north and the Gulf Stream from the south, giving it access to a large variety of larvae. From the north, cod, rockling and Atlantic herring are common. From the south come Atlantic croaker, silver perch and even an occasional tarpon or ladyfish, which may have been spawned as far away as the east coast of Florida, or maybe even Cuba. Even more extreme in distance traveled are the larvae of American eels, which spawn in the Sargasso Sea. Of course, a large number of locally spawned fish — bay anchovy, Atlantic silversides and gobies — are also collected. All of these pass under the bridge over Little Sheepshead Creek on Great Bay Boulevard at some point during the year.

This is, in part, the story of the mission of the men and women who work at the Rutgers University Marine Field Station. In part, it is also the story of the station itself. And while the station now may play a role in saving the planet, it began with a mission of saving lives.

The transitions that made this unique, long-term sampling possible began a long time ago. Over the years the old Coast Guard Station behind Little Egg Inlet has been a source of mystery, in large part because of its incompletely known history. This story begins before the construction of the present facility in 1937. It is the activities that occurred in the late 1880s and early 1900s that help to explain the reasons for its location, its demise as a federal facility and its birth as a university research center. Indeed, the story of the Rutgers University Marine Field Station would never have been possible if it weren't for the story that preceded it.

CHAPTER 1

COAST GUARD YEARS

The first lifesaving stations popped up along the New Jersey shore in the mid-1800s, soon after William Augustus Newell, a New Jersey resident, Rutgers College graduate and New Jersey governor, signed a law creating a lifesaving service and providing $10,000 for equipment to be used to save lives and property from shipwrecks between Sandy Hook and Little Egg Harbor. Often called "red houses" because they were painted red, the first two-story structures housed crews of six and storage space for equipment. By 1915, when the Lifesaving Service merged with the Revenue Cutter Service to form the United States Coast Guard, there were 279 active stations scattered along the coasts of the U.S., an all-time high. In New Jersey in the 1920s and 1930s, forty-one stations stood guard between Sandy Hook and Cape May with an average distance between them of four-to-five miles. As communications improved and motorized life boats cut response times, those numbers declined. Just 150 stations remained in the U.S. in the mid-1990s. Many were lost or closed in response to storms. Little Egg Inlet's Station 119 was one of them.

The original Little Egg Harbor Lifesaving Station was built on Tucker's Island in 1866, although some historians put the date at 1875. The station had a tall octagonal lookout tower with an integrated boat room. This "Jersey" type station served the area for more than a half century as the community on the island thrived. But during that time, the ocean was eating away at the small island. A series of storms destroyed the lighthouse on the island in 1927. Threatened by the encroaching

Temporary lookout tower and houseboat residence for Station 119 at the mouth of Willitt's Creek.

The original Coast Guard Station No. 119 was located on Tucker's Island, situated between Little Egg Harbor (top) and the Atlantic Ocean (bottom).

ocean, the Coast Guard Station was abandoned on January 26, 1933, and a 70-foot cruiser was leased as a temporary home for the crew. The station eventually washed away in 1934, when Tucker's Island completely disappeared beneath the waves — and from all maps.

The Coast Guard had already started looking for a site for a new Station 119. As part of the W.P.A program, a staple of President Franklin Roosevelt's New Deal, there were plans to build "a dwelling, boathouse and launchway, small landing dock, standard drill pole and steel flag tower and lookout tower at a estimated cost of $35,000" in the vicinity of the prior site. The station would accommodate ten men and an officer. It helped the selection process that at about the same time, a new state road was being planned — a road that would eventually be named Great Bay Boulevard.

The Coast Guard negotiated the purchase of the property for these new buildings for $1,000 in January 1936 from the estate of Joseph Wharton, who owned much of the land on a peninsula forming the northern boundary of Great Bay, an area often known as Sheepshead or Tuckerton Meadows. A map from the Coast Guard archives indicates the location of the temporary facilities on Willitt's Creek (now sometimes referred to as Schooner Creek). Temporary facilities consisted of an elevated lookout tower and a houseboat residence, all on pilings and connected by walkways. Don Salmons, the son of the builder of the Station 119 platform, recalled how once when he was with his father at the work site, he fell into the water and was pulled out by a Coast Guardsman who warmed him up in front of a coal-fired stove in one of the buildings.

The temporary facilities may have been occupied only up to 1937. Later that year riparian rights for the construction of a boat basin for the proposed station were approved. This included a channel to be dredged to a depth of seven feet from Shooting Thorofare, and a basin dredged to eight feet with a width of 100 feet.

At about the same time the new Station 119 was being planned, the Coast Guard was moving from land-based lifesaving stations to lifeboat stations. This is best represented by the development of "Roosevelt" type stations, named after then-President Franklin Delano Roosevelt. These stations were in Colonial Revival style and there were about thirty of them constructed. The new Station 119 at Little Egg Inlet was to be one of these. Construction was approved during December 1935 and work began in March 1936. The facility shared many features with other "Roosevelt Stations", including a cupola, two-bay boathouse with railway, exterior porches and a separate four-bay boathouse. Delmar Construction of Philadelphia performed the work for $49,776. Anderson Well and Supply Company dug a

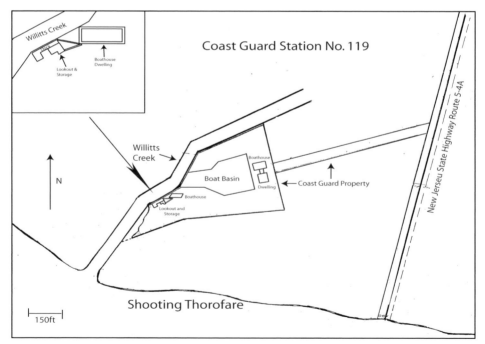

Plans for the station based on the original 1935 plot plan from the National Archives. The location of the chartered boathouse dwelling adjacent to the boat basin and temporary lookout and storage facilities are indicated along the edge of Willitt's Creek.

Early photo of Station No.119 shows a recently dug boat basin with square sides and the lack of a causeway from the station to Great Bay Boulevard.

600-foot-deep water well. The contract for the pilings and deck was awarded to J. Earl Salmons from nearby West Creek. Some of the original invoices and pay sheets are available with sufficient detail to indicate other local families were involved in the construction. The building was constructed on pilings with a deck connecting the main buildings, as it exists today.

The causeway that connects the station to Great Bay Boulevard was not constructed until a few years later. A letter from the National Archives, dated April 2, 1940, indicated that "bids for the construction of trestle (wooden causeway, approximately 1,181 feet long, from No. 119 to the nearby constructed road) to be opened at 2:00 p.m., Wednesday May 1, 1940." The contract was awarded to Tidewater Construction Company in June 1940 for $29,427. Other notes indicate that the trestle was completed and ready for first inspection in October 1940.

Coast Guard rescue vessels tied up in the boat basin. A list of vessels at the station indicated one vessel at the site in 1938, a 36-foot motor lifeboat. At the time the Coast Guard Station closed in 1964, there were four boats on site, a 36-foot motor lifeboat, a 30-foot utility boat, a 16-foot outboard and a 14-foot skiff.

Above left: Two Coast Guardsmen from Station 119 jokingly pretend to give an award for meritorious service. Receiving the "award" is Dick Handschuch; the dog is "Lady" (1954-55). Above right: Earl Salmons, one of the builders of the station.

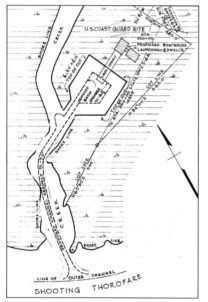

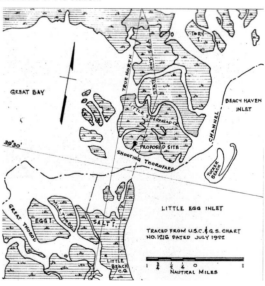

Original plans for dredging the boat basin and a channel from Shooting Thorofare. The creek length was about 300 feet from Shooting Thorofare to the entrance of the boat basin. Right: The chart indicates the planned route for the Ocean Highway (dotted line) as Route S4A – now Great Bay Boulevard. The road was intended to cross over Salt Island (now the Little Beach section of the Forsythe National Wildlife Refuge), past the Little Beach Coast Guard Station, and from there to Brigantine. The bridges to Salt Island and the southern portions of the road were never constructed.

A Day in the Life of a Coast Guardsman

We often hear of dramatic rescues by the Coast Guard, but the level of activity on most days at Station 119 was pretty quiet. The Coast Guardsmen who occupied the new No. 119 at Little Egg Inlet had temporarily been barracked at the Long Beach Station in Beach Haven Terrace. The days after the construction of the new No. 119 were, according to logbooks, spent testing the telephone line to the group headquarters at the Coast Guard Station in Atlantic City and inspecting the buildings, grounds, boats and other apparatus. Curiously, these telephone cables are still visible as they lead from under the facility, across the northeastern edge of the boat basin and appear again at the edge of the marsh as they drop off into the deep waters of Shooting Thorofare. Other records indicate that watches from the cupola were comprised of four-hour periods, twenty-four hours a day. During one of these twenty-four hour periods the watch recorded three schooners, one sloop, five steamers, six waterboats and one seaplane. When they were called for rescues, at least in the mid 1950s, it was often because a boat had broken down or run out of fuel.

During the period before the causeway was completed to the road, the logbooks indicated that the residents of Station No. 119 often traveled by boat to nearby Beach Haven for supplies. One entry included looking for the body of one Harvey B. Cramer during several days in early April 1939, but the records provided no other details. At this time the officers and surfmen were from as nearby as Tuckerton, New Gretna and Toms River and as far away as Exmore, Va., and Manteo, N.C.

Based on the accounts of several Coast Guardsmen at No. 119 in the mid-1950s, time on duty varied from the boredom of standing watches to participating in

The menhaden factory on Crab Island in Great Bay, within sight of Station 119, represented state-of-the-art technology for reducing these oily fish to a variety of products. This facility was closed in the 1960s when stocks of menhaden declined and fishing for them was no longer profitable.

NAME	TR.	TIME							Total	RATE	AMT.	TAX	NET. AMT.
E. COTTRELL	4								4	50	2 00	1½%	1 98
G. DRISCOLL		5½							5½	50	2 75	#	2 72
R. SMITH			2½						2½	50	1 25	#	1 24
D. ONEILL				2½					2½	50	1 25	#	1 24
T. ALLEN					5½				5½	50	2 75	#	2 72
W. SPRAGUE						5½			5½	50	2 75	#	2 72
B. LOVELAND							2½		2½	50	1 25	#	1 24
TOTALS									28		14 00		13 86

JOB Little Egg C.G.S.
DATE Sept 24, 1938
SUPT. J. Earl Salmons
Approving Authority

CLASSIFICATION

LOADING STONE

DAILY TIME SHEET

THOMPSON-RICE CO.
CONTRACTORS
NEW YORK, N. Y.

Transportation Exp.

A daily time sheet for workmen during the construction of Station 119. Many of the family names were typical of the Tuckerton region.

PAGE — 2 —

BY THE U. S. COASTGUARD, WASHINGTON, D. C.

TUCKERTON, N. J. — CONSTRUCTION OF TRESTLE, COASTGUARD STA.

BIDDERS	PRICE
TIDEWATER CONSTRUCTION CO., NORFOLK, VIRGINIA	$29,427.00
SPEAR-JONES & COMPANY, DOVER, DELAWARE	29,590.00
GRAY CONSTRUCTION COMPANY, MORRISTOWN, N. J.	29,654.91
J. EARL SALMONS, W. CREEK, N. J.	29,948.00
J. BRAUN CONSTRUCTION CO., INC., BROOKLYN, N. Y.	29,975.00
OLE HANSEN, VENTNOR CITY, N. J.	30,870.00
HOGAN-SAUL CONSTRUCTION CO., REDBANK, N. J.	33,450.00
GRAVES-GUINN CORPORATION, NEW YORK CITY	33,770.00
PUTCHAT & SONS, TRENTON, N. J.	33,995.45
DELTA CONSTRUCTION CO., HOPEWELL, N. J.	36,000.00
W. B. NEILL, INC., NEW YORK CITY	36,445.00
VIKING CONSTRUCTION CORPORATION, NEW YORK CITY	38,924.00
M. R. THOMASON, MONTGOMERY, ALA.	42,000.00

DELAYED BIDS

BY THE U. S. COASTGUARD, WASHINGTON, D. C.

BIDDEFORD POOL, MAINE — CONSTRUCTION OF TOWER

WALTER V. MITTON, INC., AUGUSTA, MAINE $2,341.00

Courtesy Don Salmons (both)

Copy of bids for the construction of a portion of the trestle (causeway) at the station.

occasional rescues. At that time, there were typically nine people on site, a chief, a bosun's mate, an engine man, a cook and five other regular Coast Guard personnel. From the cupola, they maintained watches around the clock over Great Bay, Little Egg Inlet and out into the Atlantic. Individuals sometimes had as many as three four-hour watches a day, and they worked six days on and two days off. When they were in the cupola, they had to punch a paper time sheet every half hour or so to indicate they were awake and alert. Most of the time in the tower was spent logging in fishing boats that entered and exited Little Egg Inlet on the way to the menhaden reduction plant, locally known as the "Stink Factory," on Crab Island in Great Bay just west of the station. There were so many fishing boats that there were often two or three people kept busy logging boat activity, at least in the spring

Don Salmons (both)

Pilings for Station 119 at high tide during construction, around 1937. Below, construction of a deck in front of the station, around the same time.

21

U.S. Department of Health, Education and Welfare

Top: View of Station No. 119 with the menhaden reduction plant in the background in June 1958. The causeway to Great Bay Boulevard is evident in the lower right. Above: An abandoned and burned Station No. 119 in the early '70s, before Rutgers University took possession of the property. Note that the roof of the main building is destroyed and the cupola is missing.

National Archives

through fall when the menhaden were in New Jersey waters. As part of their responsibility, the Coast Guardsmen also maintained radio contact with the Barnegat Lightship and with the Coast Guard stations in Atlantic City, Beach Haven and on Little Beach. During the Cold War, they were charged with reporting any sightings of airplanes because there was no operational radar at the Coast Guard Station at the time. When they were not on watches, there was maintenance to be done, especially on the boats. Once the causeway was constructed, trucks were needed to get food and mail in Tuckerton, and they also required constant maintenance. When not on duty, the men often hunted, crabbed and fished in the surrounding meadows and bays. Black ducks were much more abundant then than they have been in recent decades, and they were often dinner.

One of the more dramatic events that Station 119 Coast Guard personnel participated in was the stranding of the *Optomist*, a sailing/motor ketch, in Brigantine Inlet in December 1952. The vessel departed from City Island, N.Y., on December 4 for Baltimore, Md., with four people on board, including the owner and captain, his wife, a young man and a ten-year old boy. The weather worsened on December 5, with the wind kicking up to 40 knots with rain and fog. Small craft warnings were posted and 10-foot swells were recorded at Barnegat Light.

The vessel was first sighted hard aground at the northern tip of Brigantine Island at 7:45 a.m. on December 6 by a patrolling Brigantine policeman. The incident was reported by radio and relayed to the Coast Guard Station in Atlantic City and from there to Station 119 personnel who were located only four miles from the site. Despite the proximity, it was likely not possible to see the wrecked vessel in the bad weather. They arrived at the scene at noon, but were prevented from coming alongside the grounded vessel because of the shallow water. Eventually a boat brought by truck from the Atlantic City Coast Guard Station determined that there were no survivors on board. Three bodies, those of a male, female and the boy were later found spread along the beach from the northern tip of Brigantine Island, at Little Egg Inlet, to about a mile south. The county physician determined that the woman and her son died from exposure and exhaustion while the male died from drowning. The body of

Multiple views of the third floor of the building showing the extensive damage due to the fire (A, B, C) and a view of the first floor hall (D).

the captain was never found. The possibility for stranding of vessels still exists today at these inlets because of the numerous shoals just offshore.

Abandoned to the Elements

Station No. 119 at Little Egg Inlet, along with many other Coast Guard stations, was abandoned in the 1960s because communications had vastly improved and the range of coverage of a station was enhanced with larger boats and the use of planes. The closing was initially announced the day after Christmas, 1963. The State of New Jersey almost immediately expressed interest in the facility. Records from Coast Guard files at the National Archives indicate that the Department of Conservation and Economic Development, the precursor to the Department of Environmental Protection (DEP), requested access in 1964 and was later issued a license to use the station for marine patrol activities in February 1968.

After 1964, No. 119 was also known as a place to camp, fish and party, based on conversations with locals over the years. As a result, in the years after the closing, the station became weathered and heavily vandalized, and suffered significant structural damage, with broken windows in the boathouse and interior rooms

Fire Destroys Little Egg Coast Guard Station

WEST TUCKERTON – A fire of suspicious origin virtually destroyed the unoccupied Little Egg Harbor Coast Guard station Monday afternoon.

Firemen from the West Tuckerton and Tuckerton volunteer fire companies battled the blaze for over five hours before bringing it under complete control. When West Tuckerton fire units arrived at the scene about 3:30 they found the third floor engulfed in flames and called units from neighboring Tuckerton.

The third floor of the wooden structure was completely destroyed and the lower floor gutted.

Access to the station, which residents say was built in the 1930's, is by Great Bay Boulevard which runs into Seven Bridges Road, a network of narrow roads and single lane wooden bridges. The station is located about six miles east of Route 9.

According to Little Egg Harbor Township Mayor Robert Leitz, the station was in full operation during the Second World War.

Lack of appropriations closed down operations around 1962.

Garland Guthrie of Parkertown was the second to last man to be in charge of Coast Guard operations there. He said the station ceased operations six months after he left.

According to officials the abandoned station had been considered for use as headquarters for the New Jersey State Marine Police, but it was decided it would require too many men to staff operations.

Also consideration had been given the sight by the State under the Green Acres program.

A police spokesman said the fire apparently started on the third floor and that arson is suspected. Investigation into the fire is being conducted by Tuckerton State Trooper Edgar Cancel.

ANOTHER LANDMARK LOST: The abandoned Little Egg Harbor Coast Guard station is shown as smoke and flames billow from the third floor, where it is believed the fire started. Police say the fire was definitely of a suspicious nature.

1969 newspaper article describing the fire that heavily damaged the abandoned Coast Guard Station.

gutted. Over time, the causeway between Great Bay Boulevard and the station deteriorated such that vehicles could no longer pass, and access was reduced to motorcycles or walking.

An event that changed the rest of the history of Station No. 119 occurred on September 4, 1969, when a fire destroyed much of the building. A report filed by the Coast Guard indicated that the fire caused the loss of the cupola, destroyed most of the roof, damaged all of the third floor, parts of the second floor and a small portion of the first floor. The boathouse and garage were not affected. That's how the facility was when Rutgers University took it over from the U.S. Federal Property and Administration Service. The deed was granted to Rutgers University on Jan. 28, 1972, for educational purposes at $1 per year for thirty years. Thus, in 2002 the station formally became the property of Rutgers University.

Station Notes:
The Return of Tucker's Island

Inlets along the New Jersey shore are dynamic in space and time. Look at Tucker's Island, which existed in the vicinity of Little Egg for more than 200 years. In the mid 1700s, Reuben Tucker, of nearby Tuckerton, owned the island. As an indication of its presumed permanency, lighthouses were constructed there in the mid and late 1880s. It eventually became a resort, named Sea Haven, with two hotels, summer cottages, schoolhouses and a U.S. Lifesaving Service facility. Its demise began in February 1920 when a new inlet, called Old Inlet or Beach Haven Inlet, formed during a storm. Over time this inlet moved south and swallowed all of Tucker's Island,

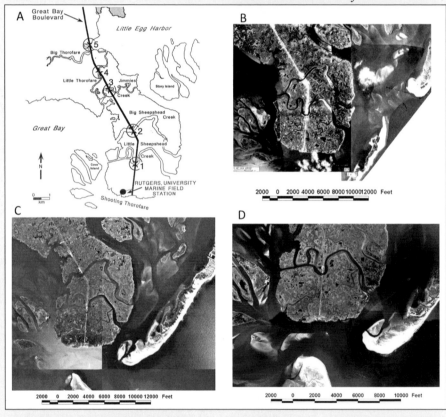

A) An illustration of the Tuckerton Meadows–Little Egg Inlet–Beach Haven Inlet. (B) An aerial photograph of the Tuckerton Cutoff to the Ocean Highway in 1930 (also known as Seven Bridges Road and Great Bay Boulevard). The lighter area indicates construction of the road. Beach Haven Inlet between Long Beach Island and Tucker's Island is evident on the right side of the image. Crab Island, the future site of the menhaden fish factory, is covered with spoils. (C) By 1994, Beach Haven Inlet is closed and Little Egg Inlet is visible at the southern end of Long Beach Island. In both of these images a cut to straighten the meandering of Little Sheepshead Creek is evident between Crab Island and the road. In 1995, a new island is evident at the southwestern portion of Long Beach Island. (D) By 2002, the southern end of Long Beach Island is beginning to wrap around a newly formed island (often called Tucker's Island).

taking all of the buildings, including former Coast Guard Station 119. The island was removed from the tax rolls in 1932, and there was no evidence of it at the end of Long Beach Island for decades. Then, in 1988, a new but smaller Tucker's Island began to form. By 1990 it had grown large enough that scores of people were boating to the island to spend time relaxing and fishing on summer days. By 1995, hundreds of boats could be seen there.

Local troubadour Valerie Vaughn told the story of Tucker's Island in an album titled "Tucker's Island and Other Story Songs." Later, she sang about the island's reappearance in an album titled "Tucker's Island Rises Again." In this version, she added a verse documenting its reappearance:

> The 1990s saw our Isle back on the rise
> From Holgate you can see it rising with the flowing tide
> You can hunt and fish and swim there
> As you watch the seagulls fly
> O'er the rise of Tucker's Island

Once Tucker's Island reappeared, RUMFS decided to take advantage of its sandy beaches as part of a larger study on fish use of shallow waters, the focus of Dale Haroski's master's degree thesis in 1998. We determined with a couple of different kinds of sampling nets that the sandy beaches acted as nurseries for selected fish species, just as marsh creeks did on the mainland side of Barnegat Bay. As part of the study, we camped on Tucker's Island so sampling could take place around the clock to determine how the types and numbers of fish varied between day and night.

Unfortunately, the island was reclaimed by the inlet and slipped beneath the waves in the late 1990s, but there is every reason to expect that it will reappear again.

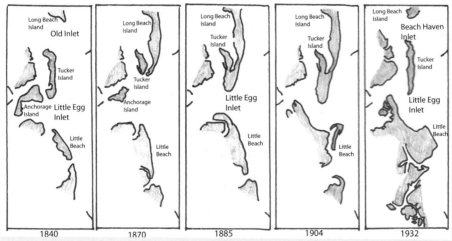

Paul Plusquellec from Shepard and Warless, 1971

These maps show coastal changes in the Long Beach Island-Little Beach area between 1840 and 1932. "Old Inlet" disappeared, then later reappeared, at which point it was referred to as Beach Haven Inlet.

27

CHAPTER 2

THE "TUCKERTON CUTOFF"

Visitors who find themselves on the quiet road that stretches through acres of salt marshes from Tuckerton toward Little Egg Inlet often stop and ask, "Is this the way to A. C. (Atlantic City)?" Actually, it could have been. In fact, the road could have been many things. In 1928, the State of New Jersey proposed, and allocated money to build, a road connecting Tuckerton and the rest of the mainland to the nearby barrier islands via an "Ocean Highway." This connection became known as the "Tuckerton Cutoff." More specifically, the plan was to build a road across the Sheepshead Meadows from Tuckerton to near Little Egg Inlet, then build a bridge across Shooting Thorofare to Little Beach, and another bridge across Brigantine (Wreck) Inlet to Atlantic City. Even before the contracts were awarded, there was talk of a large hotel, lake and a development with broad streets planned along the Tuckerton Cutoff. Yet another bridge would take the planned road across a portion of Little Egg Inlet to Long Beach Island. The bridges to Brigantine and Long Beach Island never happened. One story is that the monies for the bridges were embezzled. Another has it that the proponents of the bridges to the barrier islands underestimated the difficulty and expense of building bridges in such a dynamic inlet. Yet another version is that the people of Brigantine were never interested in a major highway through their town. The plans eventually dissipated entirely, in large part because of the development of the Garden State Parkway as an alternative to

Great Bay Wildlife Management Area sign on Great Bay Boulevard (Seven Bridges Road).

Repair of Bridge No.5 on Great Bay Boulevard after an arsonist destroyed the relatively new structure.

north-south traffic along the New Jersey shore.

The portion of the road that was completed stretched over five bridges from Tuckerton to the end of the Sheepshead Meadows peninsula. The road was referred to as Tuckerton–Little Beach–Brigantine Road, or Route S4A. Subsequently, it became known as Seven Bridges Road — apparently because the other two bridges, plus the five that still exist, were to connect it to Atlantic City — and later Great Bay Boulevard. Another possibility is that the missing two bridges that once existed over small creeks were replaced by culverts.

In the early 1900s, J. Howard Smith owned much of the property around his menhaden reduction factory, including the Sheepshead Meadows, as well as a building on Great Bay Boulevard near the bridge at Little Sheepshead Creek. It was the weigh station for the transfer of fishmeal from the fish factory by boat to truck and to market. Before the trip down Great Bay Boulevard, the trucks were weighed to determine how much fishmeal was being shipped. In the mid-1970s, Smith's company sold much of the property in the vicinity of Station No. 119, including the Sheepshead Meadows and Crab Island, to the State of New Jersey. Those 6,500 acres became the Great Bay Boulevard Wildlife Management Area as it exists today. After the Coast Guard facility was constructed, it was connected to Great Bay Boulevard via the causeway or trestle in 1940.

During the early 1970s, when an offshore nuclear generating station was being considered, an extensive study of the vegetation along Great Bay Boulevard took place because the road was the proposed site for the power transmission lines

While the bridge over Little Sheepshead Creek was closed, the initial stage of repairs for Bridge No. 4 over Big Sheepshead Creek (below) allowed RUMFS personnel to cross the bridge.

RUMFS personnel repairing Great Bay Boulevard in the late 1980s. Below: The amphibious vehicle, Benjamin H. Mabie, from the Ocean County Bridge Department, loading vehicles to use after the bridges along Great Bay Boulevard were closed.

from the power plant to the mainland electricity grid. The lack of major highway development, like that to Atlantic City, and the protection afforded by the Great Bay Boulevard Wildlife Management Area contributed to the relatively pristine nature of the area today.

The Great Bay Boulevard bridges have had a varied history as well. When originally built in the 1930s, the bridges were offset from the road in anticipation of the construction of wider bridges in the future. The three closest to Tuckerton were eventually rebuilt in the 1940s and in the 1980s, but the last two, closest to Little Egg Inlet, over Big Sheepshead Creek and Little Sheepshead Creek, were never rebuilt and are still offset. An earlier event that may have had an effect on Great Bay Boulevard and its bridges was a proposal in the mid-1930s to pass the Intracoastal Waterway closer to Tuckerton through Marshelder Channel, and from there by dredged channel to Big Sheepshead Creek, then through Newman's Channel into its current location in eastern Great Bay. This would have replaced the current route through eastern Little Egg Harbor and immediately in front of No. 119 via Shooting Thorofare. This former approach would have drastically changed the nature of the area if it had come to pass.

Soon after the Coast Guard completed construction of the causeway to No. 119, in 1940, the Coast Guard sent a letter to the State of New Jersey requesting "improvements to the highway and bridges." During the 1980s, after Rutgers University had moved into the station, the road, particularly at the end, had deteriorated to the point that large potholes made travel slow or impassable by some vehicles. One standing joke, when people complained about the potholes, was that students had dived in them and that they really were not that deep. On several occasions, station personnel, with materials supplied by Little Egg Harbor Township, repaired the portions of the road closest to the station in order to make it more passable.

One night in early October 1986, Bridge No. 5, the one closest to Tuckerton, was set on fire by an arsonist and made impassable. Ocean County deployed a temporary "Bailey Bridge" over the damaged portion to allow vehicles to pass, including those of station personnel. But access to the station eventually became even more difficult. On November 2, 1989, with essentially no notice, the two bridges closest to the station were closed to all vehicular traffic by the Ocean County Engineering Department because they were considered unsafe. Attempts to bring a generator and propane fuel to the station by boat during the winter were unsuccessful because that winter much of Barnegat Bay had frozen. Eventually, in January 1990, a large portable generator was placed on a small trailer and pulled across these bridges so that there would be power to fight potential fires with a seawater pump. Later, two Rutgers University vehicles were transported to the station on the "island" beyond Big Sheepshead Creek via an improved dock in the boat basin. This was done with an amphibious vehicle from a portion of Great Bay Boulevard near the old menhaden weigh station on January 17, 1990.

Over the next three and a half years, the closed bridges prevented fishermen, hunters and birders from access to the area at the end of the road, and scientists and other personnel from access to the station. Initially, station personnel continued daily work schedules, but it required parking personal vehicles at the marina at Sheepshead Creek and walking about a mile across the two closed bridges and the connecting road. This occurred on a regular schedule each workday morning and afternoon. Eventually, Ocean County assumed complete ownership of all the bridges, and Little Egg Harbor Township took control of the remaining portions of

Temporary walkway over repaired bridge structure on Big Sheepshead Creek.

the road. Bridge No. 2 was opened in June 1992, requiring a walk across just one bridge for station personnel. A bit later, the single-lane bridges were repaired using pre-constructed sections that were brought to the site by a barge with a crane and placed on top of the existing pilings. The last bridges were opened in October 1992. Later, in 1994, Bridge No. 5 was repaired and reopened to its two-lane status, and the bridges along Great Bay Boulevard reached their current status. Over several years in the mid-1990s, Little Egg Harbor Township paved the road. Thus, a period of limited or difficult access was finally resolved. Now Great Bay Boulevard is easy to travel and has become known as a premier location to view wildlife in the extensive marshes of the Great Bay Boulevard Wildlife Management Area.

During this time, the Institute of Marine and Coastal Sciences at Rutgers University established a meteorological tower at the site of the former menhaden factory weigh station near the bridge over Little Sheepshead Creek on Great Bay Boulevard. This tower was designed to hold meteorological instruments for the Longterm Ecosystem Observatory in 15 m (LEO-15) outside Little Egg Inlet, and later provided background data for the development of proposals for offshore wind energy.

Walking in snow across Bridge No. 1 over Little Sheepshead Creek. A vehicle waits on the southern side to transport the commuters to the field station.

34

CHAPTER 3

STORMS, FIRES, AND GHOSTS

Storms played a large part in the development and history of the area, and of the Rutgers University Marine Field Station. Storms were the major reason for the development of the Lifesaving Service and its successor, the U.S. Coast Guard, in the first place; and the frequency of storm-related changes at Beach Haven and Little Egg inlets were directly responsible for the creation of Station No. 119. The original No. 119 on Tucker's Island was battered by several storms in 1927 and 1932 and eventually was abandoned as it and the rest of Tucker's Island slid into the ocean.

A major hurricane hit the new station in 1938, shortly after it opened. One of the most devastating hurricanes ever, the "Great Atlantic Hurricane" of September 14, 1944, battered the area with a storm surge nine feet above mean sea level. Five people drowned and 100 of 119 houses at nearby Holgate were destroyed. In 1955, a hurricane caused extreme high tides that reached the level of the station's porches. Later, Hurricane Gloria, in September 1985, was reported to reach 8.8 feet above mean sea level.

None of that prepared us for what we were to see in recent years. First, Hurricane Irene teased us as it came ashore amid great hype at Little Egg Inlet on August 28, 2011. But it was only gusting from 61 to 69 miles per hour by the time it made landfall and it had little effect on the area. Many were lulled by that memory when a year later another storm — Superstorm Sandy — took aim at the exact same target. They called it the "Irene Effect." It was a big mistake.

Superstorm Sandy came ashore at Little Egg Inlet on October 29, 2012, causing damage equaling or surpassing the worst coastal battering on record in New Jersey. Sandy ranks with the northeaster of March 1962 and the hurricane of September 1944 as the most destructive coastal storms in New Jersey in the past century. Sandy came ashore in the

Coast Guard Station Given To Rutgers U.

3/4/72

NEW BRUNSWICK - (UPI) - Rutgers University Friday received the deed to the Little Egg Lifeboat Station from the federal government during formal ceremonies held here.

Bernice L. Bernstein, regional director of the U.S. Department of Health, Education and Welfare presented the deed to John L. Swink, Rutgers vice-president and treasurer at a ceremonial luncheon.

The station, which consists of 6.55 acres of land in Tuckerton, several structures and other facilities, will be used by the university to carry out an extensive program of research and education in the marine sciences.

"It's a particular privilege to give this surplus federal facility to Rutgers University, which has maintained a continuous interest in the marine sciences extending back to 1888, when it conducted its initial activity in marine biology," Mrs. Bernstein said.

Mr. Swink said the university's Marine Sciences Center would rebuild the facility, located on an island north of Salt Island and adjacent to Shooting Thoroughfare, and start a five-year program of studies comparing the estuary's productivity with others.

In addition his statement said, there would be studies on the problems of the fisheries and shell industry, with special attention to the problem of hard clam pollution.

Ocean City Daily Times, 1972

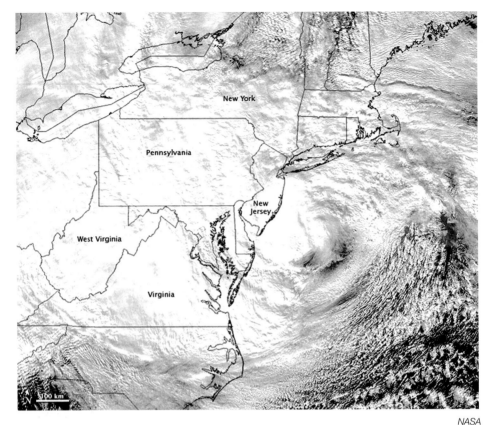

Satellite image of Superstorm Sandy along the U.S. East Coast on October 29, 2012.

immediate vicinity of the station at high tide at around 8 p.m. With a full moon, tides were astronomically high to begin with. Winds gusted to 88 miles per hour in Tuckerton. Holgate, and the Holgate section of the Edwin B. Forsythe National Wildlife Refuge at the southern tip of Long Beach Island, temporarily became part of Little Egg Inlet.

Station 119 buildings had been evacuated in anticipation of the storm. Sitting nine feet above the marshes, they escaped physical damage. Anything beneath got hammered. That included the lower portions of the causeway leading to the station near Great Bay Boulevard, the walkway to the former meteorological tower, insulation from underneath the main building, all of the docks, the sanitary system, and the sea water intake pumps and piping. A downed utility pole cut off power. The backup generator, located inside a shed at the base of the piers, was flooded. It started the day after the storm but eventually died on November 2. It did, however, work long enough to keep scientific samples frozen in the freezers until they could be moved to more secure locations. Part of Great Bay Boulevard leading to the station was washed away and closed to the general public until November 2. Parts of the station's floating docks were found two and a half miles away. Others were never found. An 18-foot boat that was on a railway away from the water's edge was

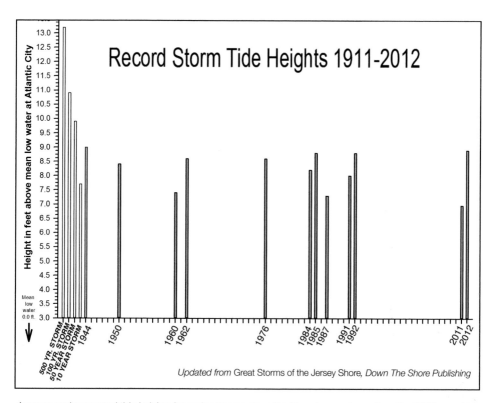

Updated from Great Storms of the Jersey Shore, *Down The Shore Publishing*

Average and measured tide heights for major storms along the New Jersey shore since the 1900s provides a useful reference point for past storms and their impact on Station 119. Below: Tide height in Mullica River-Great Bay based on selected System Wide Monitoring Program (SWMP) stations.

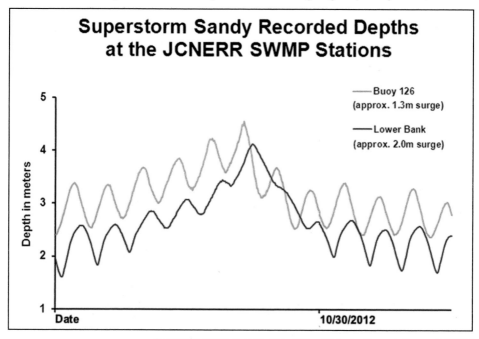

Gregg Sakowicz/Jacques Cousteau National Estuarine Research Reserve (JCNERR)

The boat basin at the field station sustained damage to docks after Superstorm Sandy. Several sheds that were on the docks were completely washed away, as were the floating docks. Below: The field station causeway the day after Sandy.

Gina Petruzzelli

View of damage to RUMFS docks from the center of the boat basin. Siding is missing from the generator shed (small building at base of dock) and the laboratory stairway.

located several days later about six miles away.

By Thanksgiving the power was restored to the station, and everyone moved back in on November 29, 2012 — although some had spent part of every day at the station since the storm. By the spring of 2014, more than a year and a half later, the repair of the electrical system had been completed, a new back-up generator had been installed at the higher elevation of the main deck, insulation under the floors had been replaced, boats had been repaired, and two of the three docks had been temporarily patched to make them useable. Just a few problems remained. The seawater intake still needed repairs and the walkways needed work. And then there's still the porta potty issue.

But it could have been much worse. The remote location just inside Little Egg Inlet and away from most centers of human habitation may have reduced the debris problem from collapsed and washed out buildings that confronted those living on the adjacent, densely populated barrier islands and at Tuckerton Beach and Mystic Islands. Many nearby lost their homes completely.

The frequency and intensity of storms may be increasing. Most notably, during a one-year period from 1991 to 1992, three "storms of the century" occurred, including the "Halloween Storm" of October 31, 1991 that caused major flooding. During those storms station caretakers were often stranded, in one instance for five days, because the road to the station flooded. However, these again had little effect on the major buildings at Station No. 119, damaging only the plumbing, electrical lines and other infrastructure at lower elevations.

The first recorded fire at the station occurred in December of 1955 or January of 1956, as remembered by a Coast Guard engineman, John Connery. It started when the well, which was located in a house under the deck, froze. In order to thaw it the Coast Guardsmen built a fire, and with the wind blowing under the deck, "it went just like a chimney." It got so bad that the creosote started boiling out of the deck-timbers. Just above the deck sat a paint locker filled with gallons of paint, next to that an 800-gallon gasoline tank, and underneath that, below the deck, a 10,000-gallon diesel tank for the boats. Toward the back of the building was another 10,000-gallon tank for heating oil.

Once the fire was started it grew quickly, engulfing many of the deck timbers. Flames reached as high as the nearby weather tower. Fortunately, Connery had just finished repairing a Chrysler fire pump, and with that pump they were able to put out the blaze. Evidence of that fire is still present in the large, charred timbers under the deck.

Another fire was caused by a lightning strike, not surprising because the buildings of No. 119 are the tallest structures for miles. This occurred during July or August of 1966, after the Coast Guard abandoned the buildings. A graduate student, Stewart Ferrell (later a faculty member at Stockton College), was camping out at the station while conducting research when a bolt of lightning hit the cupola with enough force to wake him. When he investigated, he found the cupola on fire. He was able to douse the fire after several trips carrying buckets of saltwater from

Flooding in the RUMFS boat basin. Water is almost covering the docks and completely covering the railway. The boat at the top of the trailer near the building is in the same location as one that was completely washed away during Superstorm Sandy in October 2012. Below: Flooding of Great Bay Boulevard can influence access to the field station, either by preventing it altogether during major storms, or determining when the work day starts and/or ends.

the boat basin. He likely saved the building from burning down. Crisis averted, he went back to sleep.

The most devastating fire occurred after the station was abandoned by the Coast Guard and unoccupied. This fire of "suspicious origin" destroyed much of the main building on September 4, 1969, despite the local fire company's attempts to

Flooding of the marshes around RUMFS and throughout the Sheepshead Meadows along Great Bay Boulevard can occur on spring tides and storms. The narrow line in the upper left is the taller vegetation along Great Bay Boulevard.

Photo courtesy Norb Psuty   *RUMFS*

A fire in 1976 partially destroyed much of the causeway to the field station. Right: Graduate student Walt MacDonald pulls a propane fuel tank across the ice-covered marsh to supply heat during the period after the causeway burned, when vehicles were unable to drive to the station.

extinguish it.

After Rutgers University took over No. 119 and had completed some renovations, another devastating fire took place. On April 23, 1976, the original decaying causeway or "wooden trestle" that connected the station to Great Bay Boulevard became engulfed in flames, presumably because of a discarded cigarette. The fire was so extensive that there was concern that it might burn down all the buildings.

A fire at the menhaden reduction plant on Crab Island in Great Bay near RUMFS.

A chainsaw was used to cut the causeway in front of the main deck and buildings, and the fire was allowed to burn itself out. Evidence of that fire can be seen on the charred but still functioning telephone poles on the causeway. After that fire the causeway was no longer usable, even for pedestrian traffic, so station personnel had to come in by boat or walk through the marsh. When supplies were brought in they had to be pulled across the marsh surface, even during winter. These difficulties were a major influence on the productivity of the station until the causeway was replaced.

This history of fires convinced the university to install a fire pump that could reach all of the deck and the existing causeway. While operating, it pumps seawater from the boat basin, and since its installation station personnel participate periodically in fire drills.

Other fires in the area have had direct and indirect effects on the station. Two that were related to the menhaden reduction plant occurred along Great Bay Boulevard. One that occurred in the abandoned plant in September 1991 was visible for miles. Because the plant is located on Crab Island in Great Bay, it was impossible for firefighters to reach the facility. It eventually burned itself out. Another fire occurred in the former weigh station for the menhaden plant. The remains were eventually leveled and now the site is the home of a Rutgers University meteorological station.

Perhaps the fires and storms had something to do with the stories about ghosts. After all, belief in the Jersey Devil persists in South Jersey. Just look at the amount of material, including purported sightings, on the web. Many who live in Tuckerton live by the warning that no one should go out into the "meadows" at night — meaning the marshes that stretch for miles along Great Bay Boulevard. There was

43

one technician who grew up in Tuckerton who refused to be at the station at night because of the stories that he had heard. Some stories undoubtedly arose because of the remote location and the fact that the general public was prevented from visiting during the Coast Guard years. Also, after it was abandoned, it became a popular place for parties. One visitor confided that he had lost his virginity at the station during this period. The frequent occurrence of fog at a location so close to the inlet and ocean probably also accounts for the ghost stories surrounding No. 119. This fear of ghosts in the area is captured in a George Wirth song, "The Lights of Brigantine" where he sings:

> *Down Great Bay Boulevard*
> *Well it's a two-lane stretch of blacktop. Starts at Highway 9,*
> *then it ends out where the asphalt turns to sand.*
> *Ten miles through open meadows. Reed grass growing high.*
> *You can see the lights of Brigantine, if you walk out on the strand.*
> *Across the seven bridges, pass the old boat yard, there's a burned out*
> *Coast Guard Station on the right. Everybody says it is haunted. I believe it's true.*
> *But I don't care about no ghosts tonight*

The stories persist but are becoming less common now that the paved road is frequently traveled and the unknowns of the past are replaced by certain knowledge.

RUMFS

Former Coast Guardsman John Connery (right), and Ken Able view the charred timbers under the deck from one of the fires at No. 119 in the mid-1950s.

CHAPTER 4
THE RUTGERS UNIVERSITY YEARS

The facilities used for Rutgers University-supported research have ranged from oyster shanties to houseboats to well-equipped stations. The earliest facilities for research in the region developed in response to the importance of shellfish, particularly oysters, to the economy of the region. This was especially evident in Barnegat Bay in the late 1800s, when oystering was the biggest industry in the area. Typically, little wooden shanties, or oyster houses, were constructed near major oyster beds. The Nelson team of father (Julius) and son (Thurlow) adapted this

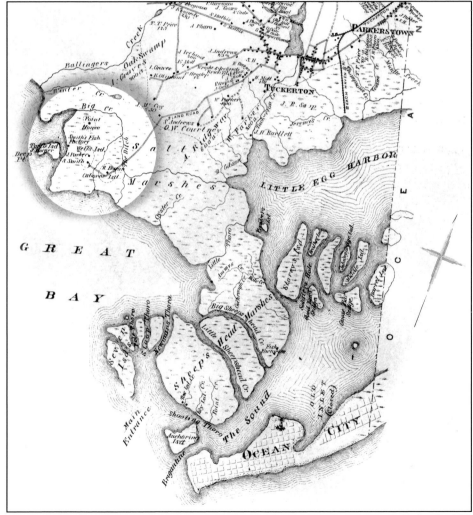

Scotts Atlas, 1876

Portion of an 1876 map of Little Egg Harbor indicating the location of Big Creek near the research facility.

45

Photograph of the Rutgers University oyster laboratory at Tuckerton indicating: 1) Mr. Mott's oyster shanty (used as dining room), 2) incubator house, 3) laboratory and dormitory "Hotel Bivalve"; 4) frame over old claire (typically a created pond in the marsh with control of water flow used to raise oyster seed. Below: Rutgers University's oyster laboratory at Barnegat and the cage for raising oyster fry.

J. Nelson 1907 (both)

approach to locate facilities near their research areas. One of the earliest locations for oyster studies in the nation was Mott Station in the Great Bay marsh meadows about four miles south of Tuckerton. It was named after George A. Mott, who owned the land. The small facility was destroyed in a storm during the winter of 1903 and replaced by Hotel Bivalve. That facility contained a combined kitchen, dining room and dormitory in addition to the oyster laboratory. These facilities were destroyed during a northeast storm in 1920 after they had been abandoned.

The exact location of these first oyster stations is hard to determine because most of the names they used cannot be found on any modern map. We do know "Hotel Bivalve" was located near the Goldschmidt Wireless Station, the first wireless station in the world, which was constructed by the German government in 1912 on what is now Radio Road. Remnants of the wireless station — concrete cable anchors, some buildings and a large chimney — still stand today. The tower was closed down in 1949 and demolished in 1955 in preparation for a lagoon development. "Hotel Bivalve" is probably buried under what today is the town of Mystic Islands, about four miles from Station 119.

Another early oyster research station run by the Nelsons was located near the town of Barnegat on Barnegat Creek, on property owned by another oysterman, Capt. Joseph K. Ridgway. That facility, which operated for decades, was of similar construction to others in these estuaries. The interior consisted of the bare bones of equipment, including a simple microscope and culture jars for observations of oyster larvae. A sailboat, the *Ostrea*, allowed the biologists to visit a variety of locations in the Tuckerton Creek area.

The most extensively used research station in the Barnegat Bay-Mullica Riv-

46

Report Bureau of Shell Fisheries, 1906

Professor Julius Nelson at work in the Barnegat Station for oyster research. Below: Nelson in Tuckerton Creek aboard the vessel Ostrea, which was used for oyster research in 1907.

Woodward and Waller, 1932

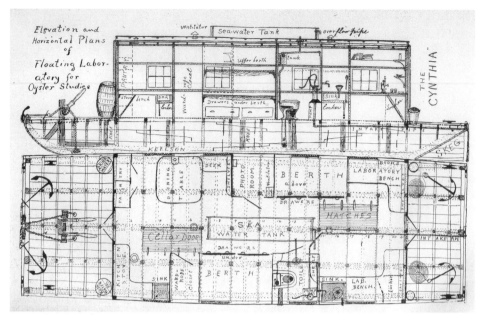

J. Nelson, 1911

Side and overhead views of plans for the houseboat Cynthia, *a floating laboratory for oyster studies. The hull length was 38 feet, with a width of 12.5 feet. It was built by Samuel Van Sant of Port Republic for $800. Below: Ready for research: The* Cynthia *was central to research in Barnegat Bay and the Mullica River-Great Bay system.*

Photo courtesy M. Carriker

er-Great Bay study area was a mobile one, the houseboat *Cynthia*. This flat-bottomed — and thus shallow-water-compatible — houseboat was constructed under the direction of Julius Nelson in 1909 and was named after his wife. It was first put into service in the summer of 1910. The well-organized and carefully constructed vessel included berths for scientists and students, laboratory space, and kitchen facilities. Various boats were used to move the *Cynthia* between moorings or provide access to other research sites for field collections. At frequently visited lo-

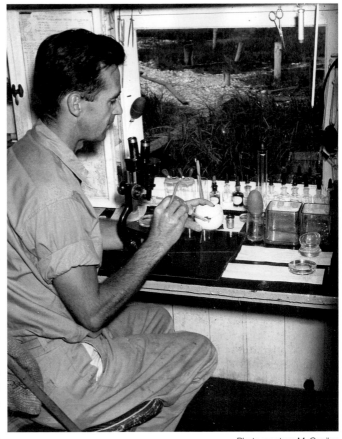

Photo courtesy M. Carriker

Professor Melborne Carriker processing shellfish samples at a laboratory bench on the Cynthia.

cations, such as Thompson Creek near Tuckerton, a variety of permanent gauges and water-circulating facilities were maintained in the creek or on the marsh surface. Typically, during the winter, the *Cynthia* and the power boat were moored in freshwater, often at Tuckerton, to prevent colonization of the hull by shipworms and fouling organisms common in higher salinity waters. During the summer, the *Cynthia* was towed to the summer's study site and anchored for the season's work. The summer mooring for the *Cynthia* varied from year to year but included Turtle Island near the mouth of the Mullica River, Thompson Creek and Edge Cove near Tuckerton, and Bayville and Cat islands in Barnegat Bay. The *Cynthia* was used by both of the Nelsons and a succession of managers and students over the next several decades.

There were occasional setbacks. In the winter of 1917 the vessel sank at its mooring in Tuckerton Creek. It was raised six weeks later relatively unharmed. On another occasion the *Cynthia* was struck by lightning, which entered one of the roof ventilators and nearly killed Thurlow Nelson. Near the end of her days, the *Cynthia* was landlocked at the New Jersey DEP's Bureau of Fisheries facility on Nacote Creek,

Portion of the interior of the laboratory aboard the Cynthia *showing plankton net, microscopes and other equipment used in oyster studies.*

where it served as a dormitory for some of Jim Durand's students in the early 1970s. Sometime thereafter, in recognition of its importance to research in New Jersey, the *Cynthia* was housed at the New Jersey Agriculture Museum on the Rutgers University main campus in New Brunswick. Subsequently, it dry-rotted, not surprising given its long life. Eventually, the Rutgers University Fire Department set it on fire as part of a practice exercise.

None of these facilities exists today. However, a remnant of early riparian grants and a site of collaboration with an oysterman named Sooy is a series of ditches dug across narrow peninsulas of marsh in the serpentine portion of the Mullica River between its mouth and the current Garden State Parkway. These ditches were dug and planted with oysters and their shells in an attempt to create oyster bottom from the "high ground" portion of the grant.

The successor to these facilities was RUMFS. Its development occurred under several leaders. In 1971, the Marine Sciences Center was formed under the direction of Drs. Harold Haskin and Norb Psuty from the main campus in New Brunswick, and Drs. Jim Durand and Ralph Good from Rutgers University-Camden. Durand became the first director of RUMFS and served from 1976 to 1986. In 1976, the Rutgers University Marine Science Center was consolidated with other university marine and environmental interests into the Center for Coastal and Environmental Studies with Dr. Norb Psuty as the director. In 1986, Ken Able moved from Rutgers' main campus to RUMFS to become director of fisheries research. The next year he was named RUMFS director. The Institute of Marine and Coastal Sciences was formed in 1989 by combining the numerous university marine components, including RUMFS, and adding new faculty positions and a new facility on main campus. This new entity, led by Dr. Fred Grassle, who was enticed from the Woods Hole Oceanographic Institute in Massachusetts, dramatically expanded the faculty, graduate and undergraduate students and visiting scientists using RUMFS.

Plankton net sampling for bivalve larvae on the bow of the Cynthia. Jim Durand (far left), the future director of the Marine Science Center (later RUMFS) at Tuckerton, and undergraduate Bob Loveland — later a professor at Rutgers University (far right). Left: Thompson Creek near Tuckerton; state-of-the-art (at the time) recording instruments used in oyster and hard clam research included a thermograph and a tide gauge.

Land based seawater reservoirs in support of shellfish

research at Thompson Creek near Tuckerton.

The Cynthia *in dry storage at the New Jersey Agriculture Museum. Below: Points of interest in the Barnegat Bay and Mullica River-Great Bay estuaries.*

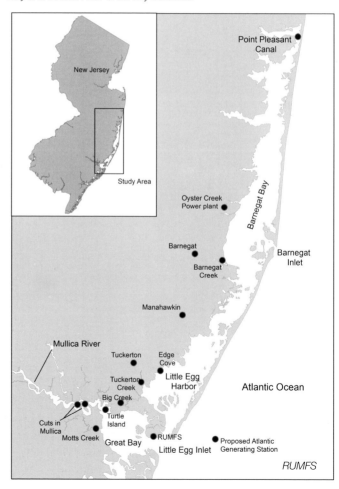

Station Notes:
The First Caretaker — Harry Pine

The remote location of RUMFS requires that a person be present there continuously. This practice dates back to when Rutgers University obtained ownership in 1972. The first caretaker was Harry Pine, an elderly and cantankerous individual who provided security during the early days when the buildings were not habitable. He lived on his houseboat in the boat basin. Previously, he provided the security for the nearby menhaden factory, but when that closed down, he moved to the station. I encountered Harry one day in the late 1970s when I came down to the station for a brief visit. He immediately accosted me, wanted to know who I was and what I was doing there. I introduced myself but he really wasn't interested. He kept repeating, "I'm security here. Want to see my gun?" After convincing him that I did not need to see it, we went our separate ways. I seldom encountered him again. After talking with other early visitors to the station, it became clear that he treated everyone equally. However, this tradition of having a caretaker continues today. Over the years, it has included full-time graduate students, part-time technicians, visitors and a host of others. None of them ever carried guns.

A Day in the Life at RUMFS

In the 1970s, when the station was just becoming established as a research facility, there was little activity at the end of Great Bay Boulevard. In 1973, the first summer the station was used by Rutgers personnel, the dorms, equipped with surplus Army bunk beds, were located on the second floor of the old Coast Guard boathouse. At that time there were windows but no glass or screens, and the mosquitoes took full advantage. The students from Rutgers University-Camden and the Haskins Shellfish Research Laboratory huddled under mosquito netting for protection.

At the time, drug dealing was rumored to be frequent at the remote end of Great Bay Boulevard, and for a while the federal Drug Enforcement Agency used the station's cupola to monitor the transactions. One time, a station graduate student was driving down Great Bay Boulevard at night returning from classes on main campus when suddenly his car was immersed in a large overhead light that followed him down the road until he turned into the station. It wasn't until he was identified as a resident that the DEA agents in the cupola called off the helicopter.

From spring through fall, field sampling is interspersed with activities such as identification of larval and juvenile fishes and data entry and analysis. During the summer there is typically extensive field sampling that, unfortunately, occurs at

Field collections of fishes in Barnegat Bay by RUMFS personnel Ken Able and Stacy Hagan were used to evaluate fish habitat for conservation purposes in collaboration with Trust for Public Land. Below: Ralph Good, from Rutgers University-Camden, led much of RUMFS marsh research in the 1970s and 1980s.

the same time that mosquitoes, no-see-ums and greenheads are abundant. The station's position on pilings about nine feet above the marsh surface cuts down a bit on insect attacks. But not so much when the wind dies.

Field sampling out of the station can take varied forms with activities sometimes focused on the nearby Mullica River-Great Bay and Barnegat Bay estuaries, and other times as far away as

56

Photo courtesy Polly Durand

Norbert Psuty (left) was director of Rutgers University Marine Science Center when former Station 119 was obtained from the federal government. Field station director Jim Durand (right) served from 1976-87.

Photo courtesty M. Carriker

Professors Harold H. Haskin (far left) and Melbourne Carriker (second from left) with Rutgers University officials at dedication of Nelson Hall (after Julius and Thurlow Nelson) on Rutgers University main campus May 3, 1968. Both Haskin and Carriker were students of Professor T.C. Nelson and important contributors to shellfish research in New Jersey.

Above: Bob Diaz and Randy Cutter from the Virginia Institute of Marine Science calibrating an underwater camera system on a sled to be deployed at the LEO-15 site off Little Egg Inlet. Right: Visiting scientist Hank van de Veer from the Netherlands examining local flatfish larvae for comparison with those in the North Sea.

the inland bays of Maryland, Delaware Bay and New York Harbor. In some instances, RUMFS personnel may be elsewhere along the East Coast or in the Gulf of Mexico, and some associated with the station have found themselves as far away as Alaska, the Pacific coast of Mexico, or even Mongolia. Nearby, field sampling adds variety to the workday. On night flood tides, larval fish are collected from the bridge over Little Sheepshead Creek. Because the tides progress with the stages of the moon, the sampling can occur at any time of the night. Once the samples are collected, they are immediately sorted back at the station. In the summer, when there are lots of larvae, this can take hours. As a result, people arriving in the morning may see others leaving for the day.

The same variation in the tides that influences the timing of sampling can also affect when personnel can get to the station. New or full moons create higher than normal spring tides, and if there happens to be an onshore wind at the time, water gets stacked up in Great Bay and Little Egg Harbor and floods the boat basin,

58

Paul Jivoff (Rider University) in the RUMFS boat basin returns from a crab collecting trip in Barnegat Bay. Below: Fred Grassle at the station when he was Director of the Institute of Marine and Coastal Sciences.

Colleagues of Bob Denno (University of Maryland) celebrating successful collection of marsh surface insects with power vacuum sampler along Great Bay Boulevard. Below, right: Ken Able (rear right) and RUMFS/JCNERR (Jacques Cousteau National Estuarine Research Reserve) volunteers (clockwise from left) Pat Filardi, Tom Siciliano and Steve Zeck sorting larval fish samples.

marshes and often Great Bay Boulevard. One time an adult winter flounder caught swimming across the road was tagged and tracked for weeks.

It's worse in the winter, when northeasters often back up water in the bays for days. On those occasions, the only access to the station is at low tide — or sometimes not at all

for the duration of the storm. In December 1992, a northeaster had winds gusting more than 80 miles per hour, with tides matching the March 1962 storm. The caretaker was trapped inside the station for five days. That storm destroyed the septic system and relegated the station to porta potties for 489 days. Restoration of the system resulted in a celebration referred to as the First Flush Fest.

On a typical day, the station is populated by academic faculty and those in train-

Stacy Hagan's funeral service and life celebration at RUMFS attended by numerous friends and family.

ing, postdoctoral fellows and graduate students, and numerous undergraduate or recently graduated students who function as technicians until they can find full-time positions elsewhere.

The numbers swell in the summer as visiting scientists take advantage of RUMFS facilities. These include individuals who are just visiting for a day, either from Rutgers campuses in New Brunswick, Camden and Newark, other academic institutions in the state, or from other states or countries. Many visit to sample the flora and fauna from the clean estuarine watershed surrounding the station. This environment also draws visitors from state and federal facilities who come to collaborate or to make effective use of RUMFS long-term collections of fish and crabs.

RUMFS residents and visitors form a close community, largely because of shared specific interests — and also because civilization is a long walk down the causeway and a long drive to Tuckerton. Spontaneous events such as "causeway bowling" often spring up after a long week of field sampling. Another, more "formal" occasion celebrates the end of the interns' summer with the Intern Olympics. Competition between the interns and staff involve a variety of events, such as the blue crab relay, a tug o' war over marsh pools, and fish sorting and identification competition. Often, when the weather and tide cooperate, volleyball and horseshoe competitions are held on a nearby sandbar.

The most solemn event the station has shared was the funeral of friend and colleague Stacy Hagan. Hagan was an important part of station life, and when she died in December 2007 of breast cancer, it was only fitting that her memorial be held there.

CHAPTER 5

REPAIRS, RENOVATIONS AND INNOVATIONS

The first renovations to the station began soon after it was leased from the federal government in 1972. The station was not the first choice for the new Marine Science Center at Rutgers University. The original choice was an abandoned building at a recently closed complex at Sandy Hook in northern New Jersey. When that didn't work out, the current facility was found through the U.S. Department of Health, Education and Welfare surplus listings.

Right away, the roof of the main building needed repairs. In the process of doing that, the third-floor roof was elevated to provide a full third floor. That was paid for by Public Service Electric and Gas Company in exchange for access to the third floor, which it would use to gather data from land-based and offshore meteorolog-

National Archives

Coast Guard Station No. 119 at Little Egg Inlet in 1954. The porch nearest the cistern is currently enclosed and serves as a dining room. Septic tanks are located on the marsh below the porch. Note the small meteorological tower adjacent to the main deck.

ical towers for use in developing plans for an offshore floating nuclear generating station. At the same time, the inside of the building was cleaned up, the well reactivated and the septic system rejuvenated. The bathroom installed in the first floor of the boathouse became the center of some activity because initially it was the only room with running water and heat. In this way it also functioned as a part time laboratory for field sample analysis. During the same period, the second floor of the boathouse was made habitable, and surplus bunk beds were used to house visiting scientists and graduate students. The porch on the north side of the first floor of the main building was enclosed and became the dining room for the adjacent kitchen. The first floor porch on the south side of the main building was eventually repaired and the railings were reconstructed to duplicate those typical of "Roosevelt" stations. Later, the cedar shakes of the station were replaced by a new exterior covering that retained much of the look of the original No. 119. It was about this time that the station was featured on the first-ever duck print for the 29th Annual

A rendering of planned renovations to RUMFS in 1992, by artist David Sylvester, who wrote, "The non-verbal dialogue between human activity and what we perceive as the natural world. The Tuckerton research facility is dedicated to the study and understanding of the environment upon which it stands with such clear and dramatic contrast that the viewer might wonder — to what extent is this field station part of the natural environment, and as such, is it beautiful?" The second floors of the old boathouse and the garage were never built as the additional weight was judged to be too great for the existing pilings.

Ocean County Decoy and Gunning Show. A tradition of painting the station in the Sheepshead Meadow marshes still exists as artists can often be seen on Great Bay Boulevard, at least until the greenhead flies clear them out in early summer.

One of the most striking features in the Little Egg Inlet area for several decades was the 122-foot meteorological tower that was constructed at RUMFS in 1973 to gather meteorological data for the Atlantic Generating Station (AGS), the proposed offshore nuclear power plant. To construct the tower and its supports, premixed concrete for concrete pads was transported by helicopter from Long Beach Island in 55-gallon hoppers. Portions of the tower were assembled in a field off Route 9 north of Tuckerton, and then the sections were pieced together on site with a helicopter. The tower's bright red flashing light served as an aircraft navigation warning system, and because it could be seen for miles, also as a navigation tool by fisherman and boaters using the Intracoastal Waterway, which passes to the east. When the tower was constructed at the station, another was erected at Beach Haven Ridge in about forty-five feet of water, where Public Service Electric and Gas Company planned to build the nuclear reactor.

The computers that stored the data from the tower were located on the third floor of the recently refurbished main building and run by Edgerton, Germeshausen, and Grier, Incorporated, a consulting company hired by Public Service Electric and Gas Company to run the project. After about five years the evaluation of the AGS site was completed and the project was rejected. RUMFS continued to maintain the tower at a reduced level of activity, but was required by law to maintain the flashing red light. Of course that meant station personnel took over the job of climbing the tower to periodically replace the light and other instruments.

During the 1990s, when the level of research and teaching activities dramatically increased, the tower was put back into operation gathering meteorological data. The tower at that point had instruments to measure barometric pressure, air temperature, relative humidity, wind speed and direction. Sitting atop the tower were FreeWave modems and antennas for communication with vessels working in the area of Beach Haven Ridge, where LEO-15 was constructed at the site of the planned generating station. Lightning protection for the tower was reinstalled in December 1997, a necessity because, as the tallest structure for miles, it was often struck during storms. The data gathered from the tower was critical to understanding many events in the coastal ocean that were influenced by the winds, including upwelling that in turn influenced phytoplankton production and the overall productivity of the region. The tower also supported an antenna that was used to pick up data transmitted from buoys attached to underwater hydrophones that detected acoustically tagged fish. This real-time data was transmitted to computers that dutifully logged in fish detections around the clock. At the time this was the most extensive listening array for fish along the East Coast, functioning sort of like E-Z Pass on the Garden State Parkway.

Over time, the tower became less central to RUMFS research and was eventually replaced by a smaller tower along Great Bay Boulevard at the former menhaden

First renovation of the main building after Rutgers University took ownership. At this stage the roof was raised and repaired to make the third floor more useful. The porch to the left of the cistern was eventually enclosed to become the dining room. Below: RUMFS with a new exterior, late 1980s.

EG&G

Meteorological tower erected at the site of the proposed Atlantic Generating Station near Beach Haven Ridge, in the ocean approximately three miles from Station No. 119. Right: Roger Hoden, former Assistant to the Director of RUMFS, climbing the RUMFS tower to repair an instrument.

reduction plant weigh station. Factors leading to the demise of the tower included the ever-increasing costs of maintaining a metal structure in a corrosive saltwater environment, and, more critically, erosion at the base of the tower. About a foot a year of marsh was being lost along the edge of Shooting Thorofare, and the erosion threatened to topple the tower into the Intracoastal Waterway or across the mouth of the RUMFS boat basin.

The actual removal took less than one day. A large barge with a crane traveled down from Newark Bay on November 20, 2007. Once the accompanying tugs maneuvered it inside Little Egg Inlet and up against the salt marsh, it took only minutes to attach the tower to the crane, cut the supporting legs, and swing it aboard the barge. Once onboard it was cut into three pieces and carried away to be recycled. The red aircraft warning light was kept and placed in the dining room at the station where it is turned on for special occasions. At about the same time, the smaller tower that remained from Coast Guard days was also removed because the foundation was crumbling.

Continued Renovations and New Construction

In the mid-1990s extensive construction and renovations greatly expanded the RUMFS facilities, and its research and teaching capabilities. The funding came

Photos courtesy Richard Coffman

Top: Richard Coffman, one of the original builders of the meteorological tower, standing on one of the concrete pads that supported it. Above: A worker at the top of the tower replaces the aircraft warning light.

from the New Jersey Education and Competitiveness Bond Act that was passed in 1988. Its application at RUMFS was organized by then-Cook College Dean Steven Kleinschuster. The renovations included extensive modification to the boat railway and the interior of the first floor of the main building. Every interior wall was removed and state-of-the-art laboratories, conference room, field prep room,

RUMFS after the construction of the meteorological tower at the mouth of the boat basin.

office and kitchen were constructed. The second floor, which had been dormitory rooms, was converted to offices, a seawater lab and a caretaker's room. At the same time an extension between the main building and the adjacent seawater laboratory provided additional office space. The seawater lab was expanded and modified to provide hot and cold flow-through seawater in separate laboratories with controlled temperature and photoperiod (day length). The dry lab building was extended onto the deck and converted from one large laboratory to five new laboratories and a small shop/freezer room. In 2011, with support from the National Oceanic and Atmospheric Administration through the Jacques Cousteau National Estuarine Research Reserve (JCNERR,) the interior second floor of the dry lab building was again renovated to include two new laboratories, an office and a conference room/telecommunications center. At the same time one of the laboratories on the first floor was further modified for autonomous underwater vehicle maintenance, mission planning and analysis.

Also in the mid-1990s, land was purchased along Great Bay Boulevard just inside the town boundary of Tuckerton where a new dormitory, warehouse and outside storage facility were constructed. The two-story dormitory included ten dorm rooms for twenty students and technicians; two visiting scientist rooms; a large common room; a library; and a freezer/refrigerator room for the large kitchen. The adjacent fenced outside yard provided space to store boats, trailers, large pieces of oceanographic equipment and sampling gear. In recent years, upgrades at the station included improved dry laboratories for immediate analysis of samples coming from the field and a clean room for analysis of fish ear bones for evaluating

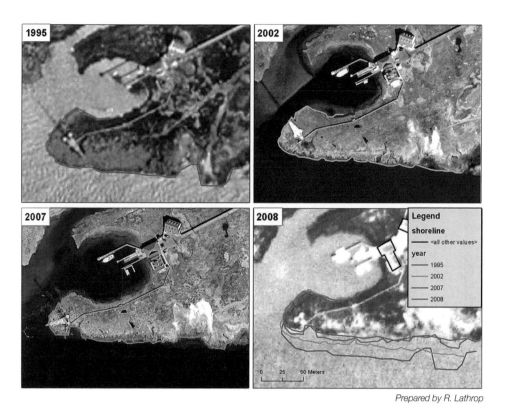

Depiction of the erosion of the marsh edge at Shooting Thorofare adjacent to the meteorological tower at RUMFS between 1995 and 2008. Below: A large barge removes the tower.

Top: Expanded research facilities at RUMFS required extending the building and modifying the interior to accommodate dry laboratories. Above: Renovations to the station during the mid-1990s provided additional office space for scientists.

annual and daily growth and environmental effects.

Vessel capabilities also expanded significantly. In 1976, the Marine Science Center purchased and christened the R.V. *Rutgers* for use in coastal areas. One of its first cruises was to the Bicentennial Celebration in New York Harbor. It was sold after a few years, when new vessels designed specifically for near-shore marine science were built as part of the new Institute of Marine and Coastal Sciences and berthed at the station. The first, the 30-foot R.V. *Caleta*, was christened in 1991. A larger vessel, the 48-foot R.V. *Arabella*, was delivered in 1996. Both participated in the intensive activities at the LEO-15 site at

Beach Haven Ridge, and in other research from Delaware Bay to New York Harbor. Other estuarine research is performed by a fleet of small vessels ranging in size from seventeen to twenty-seven feet.

Typically, about twelve to fifteen people work at the RUMFS facilities during the winter, and as many as twenty to thirty-five in the summer. One July, at the peak of the activities at LEO-15, more than 200 people from thirty different institutions were working at the site, from RUMFS, surface vessels, an occasional submersible, planes and online.

Water access to Station 119 was critical to Coast Guard lifesaving operations and it's also critical to the Rutgers University research operations. During the entire time the station has been in operation, the ability to keep the boat basin open for boat operations has been problematic. During the early Coast Guard days, the facility was regularly dredged and maintained at a depth of at least seven feet mean low water. But by the time Rutgers University began operating the station, the basin had accumulated large amounts of sediment. Access, even by small boats, was limited to high tides. Since Rutgers has occupied the facility, the boat basin and access channel have been dredged on four occasions, in 1974, 1988, 1991 and 1993.

Innovations

One of the most striking technological advances in how we are able to view the ocean came about as the result of the installation of a set of sensors in the vicinity of Beach Haven Ridge off Little Egg Inlet. The sensors were connected

Dormitory facility constructed on Great Bay Boulevard in Tuckerton in the mid-1990s houses Rutgers University summer interns, technicians, graduate students and visiting scientists.

Roger Hoden

A completely renovated RUMFS, taken from the meteorological tower in the mid-1990s. In addition to smaller vessels, the R.V. Arabella and R.V. Caleta are tied up in the boat basin. Along the walkway to the tower are several instruments including those for monitoring atmospheric deposition and offshore currents. The smallest protruding dock hosts a U.S. Geological Survey tide gauge. The wider middle dock supports numerous large tanks for holding experimental animals.

to RUMFS and the Internet via a fiber optic cable. This effort, the brainchild of Fred Grassle, director of the Institute of Marine and Coastal Sciences, and Chris von Alt of the Woods Hole Oceanographic Institute, was completed in September 1996 and quickly became the impetus for more detailed studies. LEO-15 consisted of two unmanned seafloor observatories about a mile apart approximately three miles off Little Egg Inlet. The sensors were linked to RUMFS via a cable with optic fibers to transfer information from the site, and copper wires to transfer power to the site. For the installation, a directional drilling rig was set up on the deck of the station with the drill bit controlled by computer. In order to not disturb local habitats and to protect the cable, it was drilled under the adjacent marsh, under the adjacent Intracoastal Waterway and Shooting Thorofare, to an adjacent sandbar where the remaining cable was plowed about three feet into the ocean floor to the observatory site. Once installed, the coordination of the data from the fiber-optic-linked sensors, and the sampling by ships, planes and satellites was controlled from an early version of the Coastal Ocean Observation Laboratory (COOL) room on the second floor of the main building at RUMFS.

An autonomous underwater vehicle, called a Remote Environmental

The R.V. Rutgers, *a vessel that was used during the Marine Science Center in the 1970s. Below: The christening of the R.V.* Caleta *in 1991. This 30-foot boat was designed for nearshore and estuarine operations including trawling, benthic sampling, SCUBA diving and a variety of other tasks.*

Built in 1996, the R.V. Arabella was designed for the coastal ocean and supported a wide range of oceanographic operations. Right: The route (dashed line) of the fiber optic cable from the LEO-15 site at Beach Haven Ridge to RUMFS. The internet connector there provided the ability to send the data collected to the rest of the world.

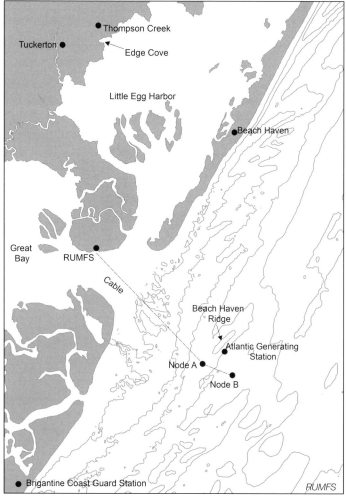

Monitoring Unit or REMUS, was added to measure environmental variables, collect zooplankton and track fish. One development was for the REMUS to simply dock at the underwater station to recharge its batteries, and a sampling trip could be extended. In addition, a variety of other sampling devices could be deployed near a node and plugged into the power source in the fiber optic cable, thus providing even more uses for the underwater observatory.

The fiber optic link provided a real time connection between the undersea world off the coast of New Jersey and the internet. It allowed scientists, engineers and educators to monitor experiments and modify them from essentially any classroom, office building or laboratory in the world.

Each node had a vertical profiler with a sensor package operated by an electric winch controlled from RUMFS, or via the internet, that provided water column profiles of temperature, salinity, oxygen concentration, light transmission and chlorophyll. Each node also had a video channel providing continuous bottom imagery, and instruments including high-resolution scanning sonar, an Acoustic Doppler Current Profiler, and a Benthic Acoustic Stress Sensor tripod. Each sensor was linked via underwater connectors to one of eight guest ports on each node. This facility operated for more than twelve years, but its usefulness extended beyond that time because it led to cabled observatories around the world.

The painting "Goldeneyes", with RUMFS in the background, was the cover for the 29th annual Ocean County Decoy and Gunning Show in 2011; it was first in a series sold to support the Tuckerton Seaport.

A directional drilling rig sits on the deck at the field station in preparation for installing a fiber optic cable from the station to the LEO-15 site, approximately three miles offshore. Below: The direction of the drill bit was controlled by a computer on the deck at RUMFS.

The control, or Coastal Ocean Observation Lab (COOL), room where LEO-15 activities were coordinated during the late 1990s. The co-directors, Scott Glenn (right) and Oscar Schofield (left) are on the phones.

A powered autonomous underwater vehicle, or Remote Environmental Monitoring Unit (REMUS), was deployed at the LEO-15 site to enhance the spatial coverage there. REMUS could be programmed to collect samples of zooplankton, track acoustically tagged fish, and record a variety of environmental variables (temperature, salinity, dissolved oxygen, pH, turbidity).

Diagram of LEO-15 nodes supported by robotic vehicles, satellites, aircraft, research vessels, shore based radars, instrumented buoys and the fiber optic link to RUMFS and its meteorological tower. Below: The installation of one of the LEO-15 nodes on the sea floor with Fred Grassle (right, Director of IMCS), Rose Petrecca (center, Director of IMCS Marine Operations) and Ken Able standing in front of the protective outer covering of the node.

Working on the docking and charging station for REMUS before deployment at LEO-15 in the ocean. Below: At the connection box of one of the nodes, fiber optic cable is adjusted by Rose Petrecca before installation.

CHAPTER 6
THE EARLY YEARS OF RESEARCH

The earliest research in Barnegat Bay and the Mullica River-Great Bay estuaries dates back to the 1800s and was conducted because of the importance of the state's commercial and recreational fisheries, which included menhaden, eels and river herring; and other species such as weakfish, croaker, sheepshead and summer flounder in Little Egg Inlet. The early fishery for American eels was so prominent Bay Avenue in Manahawkin was then called Eel Street. At the time, the eels were landed in burlap sacks, with the top of the bag tied shut and then tied again in the middle so the fishermen could hang the bag over their shoulder for transport to market. Menhaden, or mossbunker, were also used as food, something you don't see today, or they were plowed in fields for fertilizer. Early work on these fish eventually gave way to the all-consuming work of researching oysters and other shellfish.

In 1880, about 200,000 acres were used to grow oysters, and more than 100,000 people were dependent on oyster growing in New Jersey. The oysters' value was due in part to the practice of planting seed oysters from Barnegat Bay in small embayments along the New Jersey coast, in Raritan Bay, around Staten Island and on the south shore of Long Island. The economic importance of the oyster was underscored by the 1907 "Oyster Wars" in the Mullica River, where tongers clashed with guards hired by the Sooy Oyster company over access to oyster beds.

Rutgers College biology professors Julius and Thurlow Nelson were among the first to study the region's shellfish. Although their research was not frequently published in the regular journal literature, it was well chronicled, especially in the *Annual Reports of the New Jersey Agricultural Experiment Station*, which was formed in 1880. These comprehensive research studies were interrupted by the death of Julius Nelson in 1916. His son, Thurlow, had become his assistant in 1908 and succeeded him after serving in World War I during 1917 and 1918. Thurlow continued the work and trained his successors, including a younger brother, J. Richards Nelson. Thurlow retired in 1950, but by then almost all of the work on shellfisheries had shifted to the Delaware Bay.

The oyster studies began in earnest in 1900 in Barnegat Bay and the Mullica River-Great Bay estuaries. Among Julius Nelson's original observations was the discovery that oyster larvae travel with the tides. He was among the first to develop culture techniques for shellfish larvae and to determine larval duration. He advanced field experimental manipulation and identified the importance of nannoplankton (very small plankton) in the oyster diet. The Nelsons also implemented innovative techniques, such as automatic water level recorders, which were installed at Cedar Creek in Barnegat Bay in 1932, and which also made it possible to determine changing tide levels associated with the new Point Pleasant Canal. By 1926, almost all oyster planting in New Jersey was done at the advice of Rutgers University professors who focused on juvenile oyster, or spat, development.

One of the most seminal contributions of the Nelsons' work was advancing an understanding of the basic biology of oysters. This was critical because of their economic and political importance, and the legal sparring over open-access fishing. The Nelsons' scientific contributions also included some of the earliest observations of spawning, and the environmental influences, primarily temperature, on its seasonal timing. Also, detailed observations of larval duration and distribution

were chronicled for many summers. Those observations identified the effects of water density on the distribution of larvae relative to the estuarine stratification. Another set of consistent studies attempted to identify what metamorphosing larvae like to attach to. The results varied, but the shell of a dead horseshoe crab was frequently a popular choice. One of the most reliable and natural sites was the gravel substrate that dominated portions of the lower Mullica River, known as the Gravelings, in the area off of what is now known as Graveling Point. This was considered among the best oyster seed-producing ground in the country. Other Nelson studies emphasized the food and feeding of

Woodward and Waller 1932

Bureau of Shellfisheries 1906

Top: Thurlow C. Nelson, who succeeded his father Julius Nelson after his death in 1916, became a leading authority in oyster research. Bottom: Julius Nelson examining oysters with a microscope to determine the sex for culture operations outside "Hotel Bivalve".

Tonging on the Graveling oyster beds in the Mullica River during the opening day of the season in 1906.

oysters, including studies of filtering frequency and stomach content analysis.

An important component of oyster production in the Barnegat Bay and Mullica River-Great Bay study area was the evaluation by the Nelsons of sources of predation on all life history stages. There was ample evidence of predation on the larvae. One of the most important of these is the comb jellies, or ctenophore, which can appear in swarms throughout all parts of Barnegat Bay from mid-June until late in December. Other predators include blue crabs and two species of oyster drills. Predators of the adult oyster include drum fish, presumably the black drum, which crush the shells with their jaws and powerful throat grinders. In one instance, there were reports that drum fish invading planted oyster beds at Tuckerton were threatening the total destruction of the crop.

Almost a century later, consistently cited Nelson studies include treatment of feeding in larvae and adults, reproduction and early development, biology of the larvae and spat, and the effects of natural environmental factors on all life history stages.

While oyster research dominated much of the work by the Nelsons and their colleagues, other shellfish species received intermittent attention in the same study areas. Hard clams, because of the importance of this fishery, were the most frequently studied of these other species. The initial work began in 1892 with an investigation of green clams near Tuckerton. Hard clams became increasingly important after the oysters were essentially decimated. In the mid-1900s, work by Mel Carriker focused on the morphology, behavior and ecology of the larval stages of hard clams, and continued with settlement and survival of young clams. In related work, details of an unusual and large, successful set of clams occurred in southern Barnegat Bay in 1972.

Bay scallops had been stocked in Barnegat Bay in the early 1900s in the hope of establishing a fishery. It was expected that the bay's extensive eelgrass beds would provide a habitat for this species. Later observations in 1922 indicated that small seed bay scallops could be collected. In the 1950s and into the 1970s a minor fishery for bay scallops was developed in Barnegat Bay, but it's not certain whether the population came from the earlier stocking or if they were always present in the bay.

Other shellfish of certain economic significance are the shipworms *Teredo* and *Bankia*. The first instances of research on these species in Barnegat Bay occurred in 1914, when railroad bridges built across Manahawkin Bay, and other underwater wooden structures and vessels, were severely damaged by the burrowing of shipworms. Studies by Thurlow Nelson deployed different kinds of wood to measure shipworm colonization.

Black mussels were considered a nuisance in those early years because they set on the oyster beds. When they were abundant they were frequently used as fertilizer. However, subsequent observations noted that their presence caused drum fish to feed on the mussels and leave the oysters alone. Today these mussels are more commonly known as blue mussels and are valued for their food quality.

The contributions by the Nelsons and other Rutgers professors over a period of several decades are all the more remarkable given that they spent most of each year teaching in the classrooms of the Biology Department on the main campus of Rutgers College in New Brunswick. As a result, their research was limited to the summers.

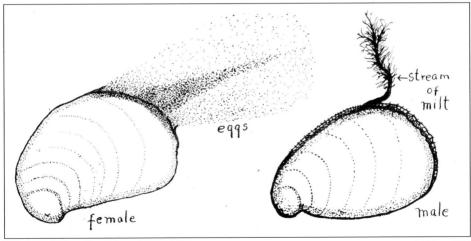

J. Nelson, 1922

Diagram of spawning of oysters with "cloud" of eggs forced out by the rapid contraction of the adductor muscle in the female and the steady stream of milt from the male.

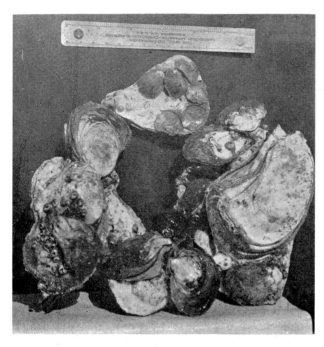

FIG. 1.

FIG. 2.

Natural oyster spat settlement on oysters from Iron Bridge, Mullica River (upper left); on gravel at the mouth of Bass River, Mullica River (upper right). Centrifuge for separating nanoplankton (lower left), and a bundle of different kinds of wood deployed to measure shipworm colonization (lower right).

T. C. Nelson, 1925

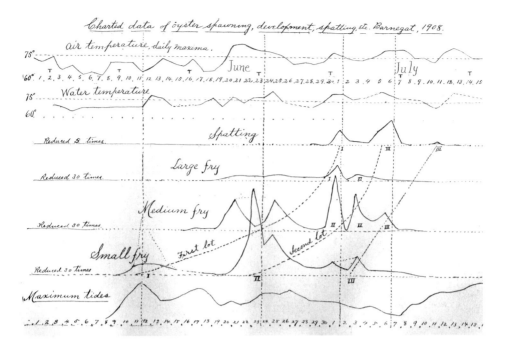

Top: Timing of the oyster's larval and spat period, relative to temperature, during the 1908 research season. Left: Oyster spat on horseshoe crab (referred to as "king" or "horsefoot" at the time). The shell was used as spat collector in settlement studies because it was "the best cultch." Each white spot is a single settled oyster.

J. Nelson, 1909 (both)

85

CHAPTER 7
CHANGE AND CHALLENGE

The changes to the ecology of Barnegat Bay are largely unrecognized by most of us living in the region, and particularly by summer residents, because of the relatively short timeline of our experience. We tend to accept as the norm only what we've seen in our time. But to truly understand what's going on in the bay, we need to look at where it's been, and what it's been through, before we get to where we are now.

In the late 1800s, oysters were critical to both the Barnegat Bay and the Mullica River-Great Bay estuaries because of their water filtering capacity and the role of oyster reefs as habitat for many other animals. Somewhere around 1915, that began to change. The decline became particularly evident with unsuccessful oyster settlement in Barnegat Bay in the 1920s, and it was continually documented for a decade. While there were many reasons behind the decline, overfishing and the disturbance of the oyster reefs by harvesting played a prominent role. The pattern has not changed. At a symposium on Barnegat Bay in 1996, featuring numerous reports on fishery resources, oysters were not even mentioned.

There were other changes to the estuaries over the same time period, both naturally occurring and human-induced. In the late 1800s and early 1900s, it was standard practice to remove eelgrass from Barnegat Bay. It was believed at the time that the thick vegetation served no purpose and was responsible for retarding oyster growth. So special machines were designed to mow the eelgrass. It was harvested, dried and used for insulation in houses, iceboxes, as packing material — even used to stuff mattresses. Today there is concern over the decline of eelgrass and the loss in ecological function that it provides.

Another major influence on Barnegat Bay was the opening, closing, constricting and creation of inlets from the ocean, which affected water circulation and salinity in the bay. The first of these was the closing in 1755 of Herring Inlet, across from the Metedeconk River, near the current Herring Islands. Then Cranberry Inlet, across from Toms River, an access point from Barnegat Bay to the Atlantic Ocean since the 1700s, closed during 1812. To compensate, in part, for this lack of connection to the Atlantic, the Bay Head-Manasquan (Point Pleasant) Canal was constructed and formally opened on December 15, 1926. The canal's impact on oysters and circulation in Barnegat Bay has been argued over the years. Early reports indicated that tidal flow through the canal influenced the upper portion of Barnegat Bay to as far south as the location of the Barnegat Pier, and it certainly increased the salinity in the upper bay. About that time, Barnegat Inlet was becoming more restricted, and together those two factors markedly changed the circulation in the upper bay, potentially contributing to the decline of oyster settlement in the bay. Or so it was thought.

J. Nelson 1901

An eelgrass cutting machine from the Navesink River, 1892. Designed to remove eelgrass from vegetated beds which, at the time, were considered the best place for planting oysters. Left: Railroad lines around the southern portion of Barnegat Bay, 1909-1923. Service to the area expanded development around this part of the bay.

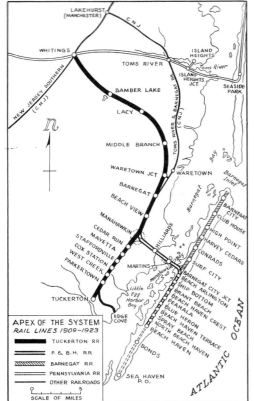

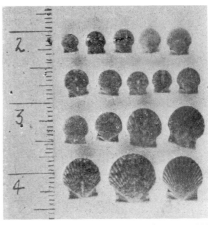

T.C. Nelson 1923

Seed bay scallops collected in the southern portion of Barnegat Bay, just east of Corklin's Island, on August 31, 1921.

87

Human impacts in the area began in colonial times when dams were built to produce hydropower for grist mills and saw mills. One such project in the Barnegat Bay watershed was the formation of Manahawkin Lake, upstream of Mill Creek and Barnegat Bay. Another in the Mullica River-Great Bay watershed was the damming of the Batsto River to form the lake at the town of Batsto. While the dams provided power, they also prevented migratory fish such as river herring and American eel from entering freshwaters to reproduce and feed. The impact of the dams has now been mitigated, to some degree, by the installation of fish ladders for river herring at Batsto Lake and at Lake Pohatcong in Tuckerton.

In another major change, Beach Haven Inlet was formed during a northeast storm in the winter of 1920. The long-term observations in Barnegat Bay by the Nelsons show that caused an increase in the salinity of the waters and a resulting increase in oyster-eating drumfish, and also an invasion of the oyster beds by blue mussels, which had previously been restricted to areas near the inlet. The inlet eventually filled in, although recently it has threatened to reform. This was most evident in the fall of 2012 when Superstorm Sandy caused the ocean and the bay to connect across lower Long Beach Island for a period of days after the storm.

These, and other forms of human manipulation, have had profound effects on Barnegat Bay. Another source of change began in the late 1880s with work on an extension of a railroad line across the bay between Manahawkin and Long Beach Island. In 1914, it was completed with private funding, and development of resorts around the bay began almost immediately. In 1926, the N.J. State Highway Department made a wider bridge across the bay to accommodate automobile traffic.

The degree to which plans called for manipulating Barnegat Bay would seem incredible today. In 1926, there was a hearing at which the Pennsylvania Railroad

Tom Belton

Changes in Barnegat Bay land use at Forked River and Oyster Creek (1931, right; and 2011, left). The Oyster Creek Nuclear Generating Station was constructed in 1964. The cooling waters for the plant were drawn from Barnegat Bay by pumping water up Forked River and through the plant; the heated water was discharged into the bay via Oyster Creek.

The lagoon community of Beach Haven West near the Route 72 causeway across Little Egg Harbor was developed in 1957. This photo was taken approximately thirty years later.

Route 72, spanning from near Manahawkin to Long Beach Island across Manahawkin Bay, consisted of fill and bridges that were expanded from earlier highways. The causeway pilings for the old railway bridge are visible just north of the bridge.

requested permission to fill in most of the bay between Seaside Park and Barnegat Pier for a railroad bridge. The request was obviously denied. Another factor driving development around Barnegat Bay was the completion of the Garden State Parkway in the 1950s. This increased use of the bay by both residents and seasonal visitors, mostly in the northern part of the bay and on Long Beach Island. The causeway bridges stretching across the bay from near Manahawkin to Long Beach Island may also have created changes in water circulation. Further modification occurred when the lagoon communities of Beach Haven West and others were developed in the 1950s.

Early changes to the salt marshes in the region were caused by the grid-ditching drainage methods used for mosquito control in the 1930s. Almost 600 miles of parallel grid ditches were dug around Barnegat Bay. More recently, another more benign form of modification known as Open Marsh Water Management is common in a continuing attempt to limit mosquitoes.

Pollution increased with industrial activity associated with World War I, and only grew after the war ended. An early example is the C. E. Howe Co.'s garbage plant at Crab Island in Great Bay. Trash from Atlantic City was barged there from as early as 1920 into the 1930s before the plant went into bankruptcy in 1934. By Thurlow Nelson's account, large quantities of oil and grease from the plant were

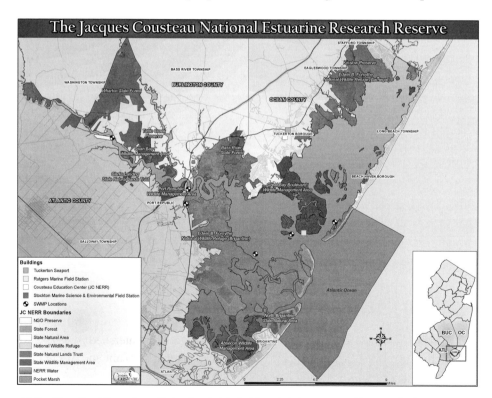

Mullica River-Great Bay estuary. Federal and state holdings help to conserve this watershed and some of the western portion of southern Barnegat Bay (Little Egg Harbor) as part of the JCNERR.

90

Station Notes:
Historical Change & Effects on Salinity

Many animals that live in estuaries, the mixing zone between fresh water and the salty ocean, have their distribution and abundance heavily influenced by salinity. For example, the ribbed mussel Geukensia demissa *is found in salt marshes throughout Great Bay and the lower portion of the Mullica River, but it disappears where salinity drops just above the Garden State Parkway bridge. On the other hand, an invasive plant, the common reed* Phragmites australis, *is abundant in the low salinity marshes of the river, but less abundant in the higher salinity waters near RUMFS. The salinity preferences of fish are difficult to determine because of their mobility. But we do know that in years when there is a lot of rainfall and the salinity is lower, summer flounder are pretty much restricted to the Great Bay portion of the estuary. In years with less rainfall, when the river is saltier, summer flounder can be found well upstream in the Mullica River. In Barnegat Bay, the number and location of inlets can influence how much salt water from the ocean gets into the bay and can dilute the fresh water. Thus, the opening and closing of inlets such as Cranberry Inlet in the northern bay and Beach Haven Inlet in the lower bay influenced not only the salinity in the bay but also many of the animals found there.*

Human activities can also greatly influence the salinity of estuaries. One example occurred when northern Barnegat Bay was more directly connected with higher salinities from the Manasquan River, and thus the ocean, by the construction of the Point Pleasant Canal. This dramatically raised the salinity of the upper bay and may have made it less hospitable for oyster settlement. Other ongoing diversions of fresh water such as dams and the pumping of groundwater may be influencing the distribution and abundance of plants and animals as the human population in Barnegat Bay continues to increase.

carried over the oyster beds on each high tide. This happened mostly during the summer when the hot weather melted the fats on the garbage scows, which then flowed into the water. Nelson noted that the entire bay was often covered by a film of oil "so thick that oyster and clam tongers were hardly able to hold the stales of their tongs, so slippery were they from the coating of grease." This was occurring at the same time of year that oysters were spawning.

One of the biggest pollution sources for the Barnegat Bay watershed was the Ciba-Geigy chemical manufacturing plant on the Toms River. This plant and its chemical waste dumpsites polluted the river's watershed from the time it opened in 1953. After decades of lawsuits, fines, environmental protests and studies of cancer clusters, the processing of chemicals at the site formally ended in the 1990s. While this ended the causes of the problem, the contamination of the groundwater over many decades suggests that the Barnegat Bay watershed continues to feel the impact.

After the area's population grew and the supply of power to these new communities became an issue, the Oyster Creek Nuclear Generating Station was constructed on the western shore of Barnegat Bay, across from Barnegat Inlet. Work on the plant began in 1964 and involved the installation of large pumps to supply cooling waters to mitigate the thermal discharge from the plant. When the plant became fully operational in 1969, a unidirectional flow was created from Barnegat Bay, up Forked River, through the power plant, with the heated water then discharged through Oyster Creek back into Barnegat Bay. The plant, the nation's oldest operating nuclear facility, is scheduled for decommissioning in 2019.

The population growth and subsequent changes around Barnegat Bay did not occur around the Mullica River-Great Bay estuary. The area is now particularly well buffered by the creation of the Pinelands National Reserve in the upper portions of the watershed. Further protections are provided by its inclusion in the Great Bay Boulevard Wildlife Management Area and parts of the Forsythe National Wildlife Refuge. This has resulted in some of the most unspoiled natural area along the East Coast of the United States. The watershed now comprises a large portion of the 115,000-acre Jacques Cousteau National Estuarine Research Reserve. As a result, the Mullica River-Great Bay is the cleanest estuary in the northeastern United States.

RUMFS

Congressman James Saxton (right, with Ken Able) was a frequent supporter of the Institute of Marine and Coastal Sciences and RUMFS activities during his term in office.

Developed (left side) and undeveloped (right side) marsh in northern Barnegat Bay.

That makes the extensive marshes surrounding Barnegat Bay and the Mullica River-Great Bay estuaries an ideal place to study marsh surface ecology and synthesize the impacts of the human population. One of the basic studies of salt marsh vegetation includes reporting seasonal changes in productivity and chemical composition of the dominant salt marsh cordgrass. There has also been extensive and internationally recognized research on marsh surface insects. Bob Denno, his students and collaborators performed this work along Great Bay Boulevard for more than thirty years. Denno began his post-doctoral work at Rutgers University in 1973, and within a year he was hired as an assistant professor. During that time he was introduced to salt marshes while studying the ecological effects of insecticides and insect systematics. Soon after he moved to the University of Maryland, but he continued to work on marshes along Great Bay Boulevard. He and his colleagues were often seen "vacuuming" the marsh grasses to sample insects.

From 1973 to 1976, an extensive study looked at the effect of a large lagoon development, Beach Haven West. To create Beach Haven West, the developers dredged numerous dead end canals along and around Mill Creek in an area formerly known as the Remson Meadows near Manahawkin. Beginning in 1957, more than 104 canals were created over an area of 2.2 square miles, transforming the natural marsh into a major lagoon housing development. The study of the ecological impact to the area was a multi-institutional effort between Rutgers University, with its Marine Field Station and Camden and New Brunswick campuses, and the New Jersey Department of Environmental Protection and its Bureau of Fisheries Management and Bureau of Wildlife Management. The research compared the lagoon development that was dug into the marsh surface to nearby undisturbed marshes. The studies included hydrography, nutrients, water quality, primary production, benthic invertebrates, zooplankton, food webs, fish and shellfish, marsh surface animals, and the harvest of fish and crabs. The extensive findings developed an understanding of the complex food webs in both altered and unaltered systems and clearly indicated that the physical-chemical environment of the lagoons differed dramatically from the natural marsh creeks.

The most important finding was that the restricted circulation in the lagoons caused low oxygen concentrations that were harmful to most aspects of the lagoon ecosystem. In addition, the loss of the marsh surface, through the dredging of the lagoons and burial of the marsh with the dredge material, accounted for loss of system productivity. The ecological findings were indicative of consequences to other lagoon developments, such as in the Mystic Islands area on Great Bay, where drag lines were used to create canals and provide fill on top of the marsh surface to elevate the land for housing. These same types of alterations of the marsh surface have occurred all over Barnegat Bay's western shore.

The upstream portions of estuarine watersheds are critical to the downstream water quality. Fortunately, the Pine Barrens watershed has been protected and studied extensively. This, and subsequent conservation and research, has set the stage for a broader understanding of the Barnegat Bay and Mullica River-Great Bay estuaries.

Today Barnegat Bay, because of its unique qualities, is part of the National Estuary Program as the Barnegat Bay Partnership. Current efforts are aimed at resolving the effects of population growth, particularly the excess nutrients entering the watershed and estuary.

Other syntheses for the Mullica River and Great Bay resulted from their inclusion in the Jacques Cousteau National Estuarine Research Reserve, a partnership formed in 1997 between Rutgers University, Richard Stockton College of New Jersey, the U.S. Fish and Wildlife Service and others. The reserve is exceptional because much of the land is managed by numerous federal and state protections and thus is valued by many interested in conservation of New Jersey resources. These syntheses also provide for evaluation of impacts between the relatively heavily populated Barnegat Bay estuary and the very lightly populated Mullica River-Great Bay estuary.

CHAPTER 8
THE 1970S: A NEW ERA OF RESEARCH

The 1970s ushered in a new era of active marine research as two power plant-related studies broadened our understanding of the ecology of the Barnegat Bay and Mullica River-Great Bay estuaries. The first evaluated the potential impacts of the nation's first nuclear power plant on Barnegat Bay. The second was an environmental impact study for a proposed floating nuclear power plant, the Atlantic Generating Station, off of Little Egg Inlet.

Rutgers University faculty and students started studying the area of the Oyster Creek nuclear plant on the western shore of the bay just north of Barnegat Inlet in 1963, a year before construction began, and continued through 1984, covering the first fifteen years of commercial operation. Much of the focus was on the central portion of the bay, with an emphasis on the immediate vicinity of the plant

between Cedar and Double creeks. The most intensive studies took place in the modified Forked River and Oyster Creek, which served as the intake and discharge, respectively, for the cooling waters for the plant. Researchers looked at the physical environment, the macroflora and the fauna, with a particular focus on benthic fauna, shellfish, shipworms and fouling organisms. There were extensive analyses of phytoplankton and zooplankton, and predation by an abundant ctenophore, or comb jelly, as well as the ecologically important bay anchovy.

For the first time, these studies included a focus on fish and found a diverse fauna that included resident fishes and migratory warm-weather and cold-weather species. In addition, there was an effort

NJDEP file photo
New Jersey Department of Environmental Protection personnel examining small artificial reefs for juvenile fish.

to synthesize the available information on predator-prey relationships and pollution effects with much of the data collected from the early 1960s through the early 1980s. Among the findings: the Atlantic tomcod, a northern species, virtually disappeared, while the Atlantic croaker, a southern species previously unseen in the area, became abundant in the bay.

But the attempts to pinpoint the power plant's impact on the bay ran into an insurmountable problem. The bay had been bombarded from so many directions

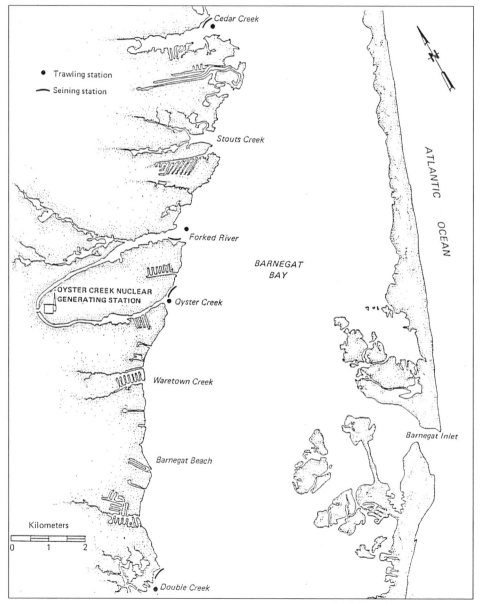

Modified from Kennish and Lutz 1984

Oyster Creek Nuclear Generating Station in Barnegat Bay, between Cedar and Double creeks.

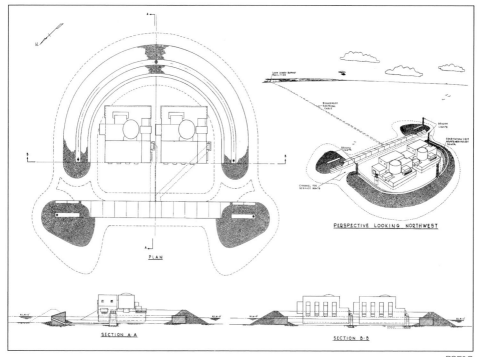

Several schematics of the proposed Atlantic Generating Station, a floating nuclear power plant, and its associated breakwater outside Little Egg Inlet.

— from residential development, to commercial and recreational fishing, to the dredging of channels and waste disposal — it was impossible to determine just which was responsible for what.

The other studies involved the Atlantic Generating Station power plant, which was proposed for waters on the inner continental shelf, a little more than two miles off Little Egg Inlet. The generating units were to be placed on a floating barge and protected by a large semicircular breakwater in thirty to forty-four feet of water. The efforts to evaluate the potential impacts covered the period from 1971 through 1975 and focused largely on fish and organisms that live on the ocean floor. The studies extended to the Barnegat Bay and the Mullica River-Great Bay estuaries and contributed to our understanding of the fish, zooplankton, and benthic fauna there. Evaluations of sport fisheries and commercial shellfisheries were also included. Some of the efforts extended to 1977, before Public Service Electric and Gas Company decided in 1978 to abandon the project due to less-than-anticipated growth in electricity demand. While the data coming from these studies was voluminous, there was little attempt at synthesis at the time. But collections of the preserved fish were deposited as voucher specimens in the Academy of Natural Science of Philadelphia, now part of Drexel University, and incorporated into later syntheses. More recent analyses have described the fish habitats at the same site because it was the location of the terminus for the LEO-15 fiber optic link.

Paul Hamer examining fish collections at the Nacote Creek laboratory of the New Jersey Department of Environmental Protection.

Other research of the estuaries has been conducted by the state Bureau of Marine Fisheries, which moved its facilities from a former Coast Guard Station on Long Beach Island to its current facility on Nacote Creek on the Mullica River in 1964. Its estuarine fish studies included those of the Mullica River-Great Bay estuary and Barnegat Bay. It looked at larval fish entering the inlets for the estuaries, and studied estuarine food webs based on stomach content analysis. Another study described the foul hook fishery on striped bass in the Mullica River. The studies emphasized summer flounder and included numerous surveys of the fisheries for this species during the 1970s and 1980s, as well as the occurrence and distribution of the larvae and juveniles. Similar studies emphasized winter flounder life history, movements and age structure. Others focused on striped bass migration and the location of spawning sites for anadromous fish. More studies focused on hard clam and oyster transplant efforts, and others have evaluated the environmental impacts of dredge holes in Barnegat Bay.

One of the most intensive studies involved artificial reefs in state waters. Numerous artificial structures from ships to tanks, to rubble and tire units have been sunk to create habitat for fish, crabs, lobsters and other arthropods, annelid worms and mollusks.

Other studies include general marine ecology, marine mammal and invertebrate biology, and geology by marine scientists at Richard Stockton College of New Jersey.

CHAPTER 9
EARLY RESEARCH IN UNIQUE LANDSCAPES

Many excellent research sites are located around the Rutgers facility in the Mullica River–Great Bayand Barnegat Bay estuaries, and its location in Little Egg Inlet provides immediate access to the adjacent Atlantic Ocean. These habitats include unaltered salt marshes adjacent to the station, and easy access to the rest of the Great Bay Boulevard Wildlife Management Area and the Forsythe National Wildlife Refuge. Bay, lagoon, marsh creek and ocean waters are all within minutes. That's made the Marine Field Station a focal point for estuarine and marine researchers from Rutgers and numerous other institutions inside and outside the region. The following characterizes the early Rutgers University research efforts.

Estuarine Nutrients

In the early days of RUMFS, extensive studies of the relatively unaltered Mullica River-Great Bay indicated even minute sources of nitrogen from the watershed influence phytoplankton production. This is the first time that this relationship was fully understood and is the basis for many studies of estuarine eutrophication, or abundant plant growth caused by excess nutrients. Additional studies suggested that nitrogen enters this system and other New Jersey coastal estuaries as nitrate nitrogen in the upper drainages and leaves the estuary to the inner shelf as organic nitrogen. However, they show a spatial variation in the nitrogen supply, with some upstream tributaries providing more nitrogen when they are disturbed by agriculture or urbanization. More comprehensive but unsynthesized nutrient data are available from the ocean to tidal freshwater in the same estuary. The issue of eutrophication was detected in these early studies, and it continues to be studied today with the increasing realization that nitrogen from the atmosphere is a significant contribution to these estuaries. Other studies found that there is relatively low freshwater flow, which accounts for the stable salinity gradient in most of the bay and lower river.

Salt Marsh Dynamics

Some of the earliest studies in the region were insightful because they showed the belowground salt marsh cordgrass production was as dynamic as that above ground. Also, studies of increased marsh flooding, as is occurring with sea level rise, began on marsh vegetation in the 1970s by Ralph Good's students and colleagues. Much of this effort focused on experimental plots in the immediate vicinity of the station. Some plots received increased flooding, while others got enhanced drainage and others were unaltered. Specific studies focused on plant community structure, soil chemistry and salt marsh cordgrass productivity. They demonstrated the effects of hydrology on the marsh surface. Other studies demonstrated the effects of tidal regime and marsh elevation on plant detritus decomposition and organic matter cycling in salt marshes. Unfortunately, much of this work was not completed due to the death of Ralph Good in December 1991.

Subsequently, other baseline studies included mapping the marsh surface in the Great Bay Boulevard Wildlife Management Area. These maps indicate the high abundance of marsh pools and creeks, which is presumably the natural condition for New England-type marshes in general.

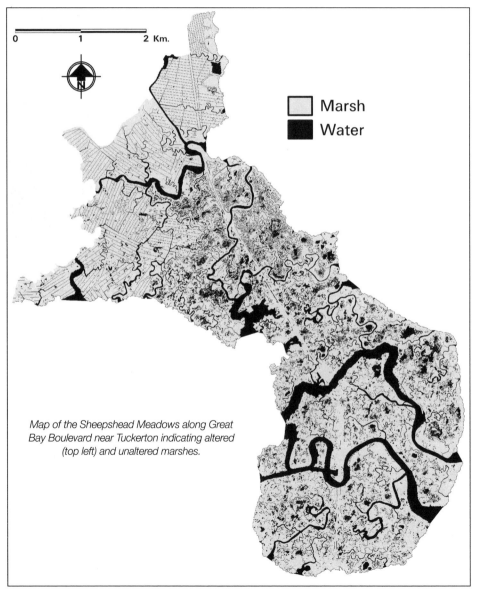

Map of the Sheepshead Meadows along Great Bay Boulevard near Tuckerton indicating altered (top left) and unaltered marshes.

Extensive, largely unaltered salt marsh near RUMFS. Great Bay Boulevard is on the upper right with the causeway leading to the station in the center. The bridge (top of photo) over Little Sheepshead Creek is the site of extensive sampling for larval fishes.

Bird and Fish Interactions, and Terrapins

Barrier island and salt marsh birds were studied extensively in the vicinity of RUMFS beginning in the 1960s. Many of these studies were conducted by Colin Beer and his students from Rutgers University–Newark and took place out of the abandoned Coast Guard Station on Little Beach, just south of Little Egg Inlet. These studies focused on the ecology and behavior of gulls and other marsh nesting birds. When that station burned down in 1976, at least one study continued at Station 119. This study focused on the barn swallows that nested under the station every summer. The colony is still active as of this writing. Concurrent investigations by Joanna Burger of Rutgers University continued with an emphasis on gulls and other coastal nesting birds. These studies continued into the 2000s with a focus on bird-fish feeding interactions through courtship, nesting and fledging. Other studies of seasonal abundance focused on use of marsh edge intertidal areas.

These interests included other marsh-nesting animals such as diamondback terrapin. In recent years, studies of the diamondback terrapin along Great Bay Boulevard and elsewhere in Barnegat Bay emphasize sex-based dispersal and fidelity, and road effects (Great Bay Boulevard) on nesting activity and mortality.

Above: Experimental salt marsh plots near RUMFS that helped to evaluate the effect of marsh flooding by comparing plots with more flooding than normal, less flooding through enhanced drainage, as well as control plots. Below: Eggs from a diamondback terrapin nest that were removed because they were laid in a patch of sand on the paved portion of Great Bay Boulevard.

Jackie Toth Sullivan

Bottlenose dolphins were studied at RUMFS to compare their use of nearshore and estuarine waters in southern New Jersey from spring through fall.

Station Notes: Dolphin No. 56

Bottlenose dolphins are regular summer visitors to the coast of New Jersey. One of the most iconic was No. 56. This male got branded with the number

using liquid nitrogen on his dorsal fin in 1979 in east-central Florida's Indian River Lagoon as part of a National Marine Fisheries Services survey. He was estimated at the time to be around twelve years old, based on the rings in a pulled tooth. He spent most of his time in the same lagoon for the next fifteen years. But beginning in the 1980s, he began spending summers exploring the East Coast from Florida to as far north as Long Island. He was spotted at least fifty times in New Jersey, and several times by our researchers. One such sighting came on October 22, 2003, when he was photographed by Jackie Sullivan in the Intracoastal Waterway adjacent to RUMFS, as part of her research on dolphin populations. The last sighting in New Jersey was in 2011, and it's believed that No. 56 died of old age. Other bottlenose dolphins continue to visit the area and are often visible in the summer.

103

CHAPTER 10

TO THE PRESENT:
ESTUARINE FISH RESEARCH THEMES

Researchers at RUMFS have been intrigued for years by how fish use estuaries. They have been attempting since the 1980s to characterize the species and life history stage composition of fish in marsh pools, intertidal zones, subtidal creeks and bays. To do so, they need to employ different sampling techniques. Pop nets capture fish in the water column. Weirs, block nets and seines collect both water column and bottom fish. Other habitats require specific devices, such as throw traps, otter trawls, subtidal and intertidal traps, and "acoustic video" from mobile platforms such as kayaks. In all, more than 49,000 samples of fish have been collected in the Mullica River-Great Bay and Barnegat estuaries over the last twenty-five years. Other approaches, such as caging fish in a variety of habitats, provide a comparison of growth rates, an important index of habitat quality. Many efforts include a focus on killifish, a group of small fish that are abundant in marshes. Together the studies present a comprehensive picture of the fish and fauna that use the Mullica River-Great Bay estuary and thus provide a baseline for comparison to more threatened estuaries.

An increasing emphasis at RUMFS is being placed on fish recruitment and the processes that influence the number of survivors in the early life stages. It employs sampling for larvae and juveniles, analysis of growth histories based on fish otoliths (ear bones), experiments on predation by benthic invertebrates, and telemetry studies to measure movements and population turnover rates for juveniles. Together these studies are providing insights into the factors affecting survival and population fluctuations of estuarine-dependent fish.

Synthesis of Life History and Ecology

While many of the fish that occupy the Barnegat Bay and Mullica River-Great Bay estuaries are economically and ecologically important, there are surprising gaps in our understanding of their life history and ecology. Filling these gaps and synthesizing the available information has been one of the major goals of RUMFS personnel, graduate students, undergraduate students, technicians and summer interns since 1986. To that end, numerous theses and dissertations, peer-reviewed publications and technical reports have summarized the efforts. Most importantly, two books, written by Kenneth W. Able and Michael P. Fahay, synthesize this information. The first, *The First Year in the Life of Estuarine Fishes in the Middle Atlantic Bight* (Rutgers University Press, 1998) focused on estuarine fish from Cape Cod to Cape Hatteras, with much of the original data coming from the Mullica River-Great Bay and Barnegat Bay estuaries. The second, *Ecology of Estuarine*

Marsh pool fish were sampled with a towed mini-seine.

Fishes: Temperate Waters of the Western North Atlantic (Johns Hopkins University Press, 2010) incorporated all of the available information on an expanded list of species and summarized what we know about their life history stages, including a special emphasis on reproduction, larval supply, growth, mortality, habitat use, predator and prey interactions, migrations and effects of climate change.

The ongoing studies of fish in estuarine habitats clearly show that use is highly seasonal, with most species abundant from spring through fall and particularly in the summer. Much of the abundance at the warmest temperatures is due to reproduction in the estuary or movement of larvae and juveniles into the estuary after spawning in the ocean. Once in the estuary many species take up residence along their preferred portion of the salinity gradient from the high salinity at the mouth of estuaries, such as at Little Egg Inlet, up to tidal and non-tidal freshwaters in the upper estuary.

Many of the efforts to determine patterns of habitat use in the estuaries have revolved around the effects of the invasive *Phragmites* and its impact on marsh surface habitats and fish. Because RUMFS has easy access to clean, high salinity water, behavioral studies are often conducted, including in the wet lab "basement" amid the foundation pilings under the station laboratories.

One of the most insightful series of studies by RUMFS faculty and students involved tagging juvenile and adult fish across several species with acoustic tags. These fish were tracked across multiple estuaries, through many years and seasons, day and night. It represents one of the most intensive efforts of its kind, and as a

Large and small seines have been used to capture fish on ocean beaches and in marsh creek habitats. Below: Intertidal "basement" laboratory at RUMFS used to observe behavior of fish in tethering experiments.

106

result, we now have an improved understanding of coastal migrations, and we've learned that estuarine fidelity over months and years is common. We now know that site fidelity is common to particular locations and habitats, and that storms affect behavior by prompting some fish to leave the shallow estuary for the relative calm of the deeper ocean. We have also been provided an improved understanding of the seasonality of fish predators such as striped bass, bluefish and weakfish in these estuaries. These base studies have helped to enhance the acoustic tracking technology such that tracking with an autonomous underwater vehicle is now possible.

Insights from Long-Term Data

One of the benefits of place-based research is the ability to collect data over the long term. This is becoming more critical as we assess the effects of climate change, sea level rise, and other manmade and natural impacts. One of the earliest and continuously collected data sets is for water temperature at the mouth of the station's boat basin. This data set, which began in 1976 and continues today, clearly shows the average annual estuarine temperatures rising, especially since 2000.

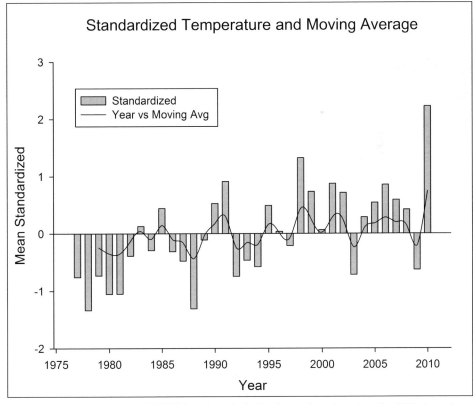

Temperatures at the mouth of RUMFS boat basin indicating increasing values since the 1970s based on comparison with the long-term average ("zero" line).

Other studies have followed the decline of eelgrass in Barnegat Bay. Still others have focused on the fauna, with most of the emphasis on fish, but also including shorebirds, bay scallops and bottlenose dolphins, and one conducted with Stockton faculty and students on harbor seals in the vicinity of Little Egg Inlet. Other shorter term studies addressed larval lobster, blue crab life history and ecology, and scallop reproduction and settlement sites.

The emphasis on fish includes a consistent monitoring of larvae and juveniles since 1989. The larval fish time series is based on sampling with plankton nets at Little Sheepshead Creek Bridge on Great Bay Boulevard on nighttime flood tides. All of the preserved samples are identified, measured under microscopes and arranged by date in vials of larvae that are continuously accumulating in the small laboratory at the field station. Samples are more abundant from late spring to early fall, and less so from late fall through winter. This seasonality results from the broad temperature range along the New Jersey coast.

Early spring catches are dominated by winter flounder. Summer and fall bring the greatest array, including menhaden, anchovies, pipefish and a number of tropical strays that include butterflyfish and an occasional tarpon and ladyfish. In the fall, the larvae of the important summer flounder begin to show up. In the winter, larval collections are largely Atlantic herring, and the larvae (glass eels) of the American eel begin to appear. Then the cycle starts over. And the sampling continues.

The composition, size and abundance of larvae entering the estuary provide important indices that help determine the status of populations. The time series are critically important, especially during a period of climate change, and they provide an efficient means of untangling the complex life histories of fish. We now know the annual timing of larval fish in general, as well as for summer flounder, winter flounder and Atlantic menhaden. Data that are not typically available were obtained using techniques such as sampling under the lights in the RUMFS boat basin at night. The continuing availability of this valuable data is made possible by our location at RUMFS, which allows samples to be sorted immediately, an advantage of being in the right place.

Two other time series focusing on juvenile fish have also been invaluable. The year round sampling, two to five times a week since 1992, with traps in the RUMFS boat basin, has shown changes in abundance, fidelity to individual sites by black sea bass and tautog, winter mortality for smaller individuals of a variety of species, and the lack of effects of boat basin dredging. Otter trawl collections since 1989 are another source of juvenile fish data on habitat use by multiple species throughout the Mullica River-Great Bay estuary. These collections, typically done during July and September, have enhanced our understanding of estuarine juvenile fish in a variety of ways, including the effects of climate change and how that is changing the fauna with fewer northern and more southern fish species as temperatures continue to warm.

Station Notes:
Tracking Fish with E-Z Pass

We study some fish so closely we get to know them as individuals. Over the years, we have surgically implanted acoustic tags into weakfish, bluefish, black sea bass, winter flounder and others, but the species we have followed most frequently is striped bass. We have tagged them in Great Bay and the Mullica River and followed their movements with underwater receivers, not unlike the E-Z Pass system which records passage through toll booths from inside your car. As a result, we know rather well the habitats that these individuals use and how long they use them. When colleagues in Maine set up a similar system in the Saco River, we took advantage of the opportunity to track individual striped bass more extensively. For example, one individual named "Bachelor" (above) was tagged on May 2, 2003, at Pebble Beach, near Graveling Point in Great Bay. The twenty-two-inch bass was detected again three days later upstream in the vicinity of the Garden State Parkway bridge, and again on the same day as far upstream as Lower Bank. It had to be swimming at a rate of about a quarter mile per hour. Over the next few days it moved back and forth between these general locations as if it were either searching for a spawning partner or following bait fish. It was next detected downstream in the vicinity of RUMFS and in Little Egg Inlet on May 13, 2003. The next detection was in the Saco River in Maine on August 14 of the following year. It was not observed again until a year later, when it was found back in Great Bay on April 14, 2005. A month and a half after that, Bachelor was caught in Cape Elizabeth State Park, Maine, by an angler who sent us the tag for identification. This well-traveled striped bass covered more than 1,500 miles between New Jersey and Maine during the two years it carried the tag.

Estuarine and Ocean Comparisons

The work at RUMFS, surrounded by the Jacques Cousteau National Estuarine Research Reserve and the Barnegat Bay National Estuary Program, has provided the background for broader comparisons to other, more impacted estuaries. Understanding estuarine structure and function across geographic areas is a critical need for the conservation and management of the diverse estuaries along the Jersey Shore and the entire East Coast.

Using the Little Egg Inlet as a baseline, RUMFS has collaborated with others to compare the kinds and numbers of larval fish species. Those studies provided insights into the factors influencing larval dispersal and population fluctuation for several estuarine species of recreational and commercial importance, such as summer flounder. The same baseline at RUMFS provides perspective for an understanding of how the modification of urban shorelines such as in the New York Harbor can alter fish populations. A series of studies designed to evaluate commercial pier effects clearly demonstrated how shading under piers reduced the number of fish species, and their feeding and growth.

In the Delaware estuary, the large-scale restoration effort designed as mitigation for Public Service Electric & Gas Co. nuclear power plants has improved understanding of salt marsh restoration, in large part by comparing the restored marshes to the relatively unaltered marshes in the Mullica River-Great Bay estuary. A good example of this is the ongoing evaluation of the success of restoration of former salt hay farms and invasive *Phragmites* removal and the restoration of salt marsh cordgrass. The linkages between New Jersey estuaries and the adjacent Atlantic Ocean were clarified as the result of an unusual event that produced low oxygen conditions off New Jersey in 1976. High river runoff, relatively few

Plankton net sampling on night flood tides for larval fishes has occurred weekly since 1989. The study is a long-term evaluation of supply to Mullica River-Great Bay and Barnegat Bay estuaries through Little Egg Inlet.

Throw traps used to capture fish and crabs in shallow estuarine waters. Below: Caging experiments in the RUMFS boat basin to determine overwinter survival of juvenile summer flounder.

Station Notes: Rare Fish Visit RUMFS

In an attempt to find out more about the fish that live in the area, we began early on collecting in our boat basin with "minnow" traps. We are frequently surprised by what we catch. Often, fish that we do not typically see in these waters as adults show up as juveniles. These include species from the north, such as pollock, which typically show up in colder temperatures in the spring. In recent years, with increasing water temperatures, especially in late summer, we often see the juveniles of southern species in the traps. This includes gag grouper and butterflyfish, both of which reproduce south of Cape Hatteras, North Carolina. Other species from the south include gray snapper and an occasional tarpon and bonefish, both of which probably result from spawning off the east coast of Florida. Many of these species from the south are most likely transported to the north via the Gulf Stream, then leave the stream and swim inshore or are carried inshore by filaments of water from the Gulf Stream. They then enter Great Bay and eventually end up in our boat basin and in our traps.

Besides deepening our understanding of the dispersal of these juvenile fish, our trapping became even more illuminating when we mounted a small camera in the mouth of one of the traps and hardwired the camera to a monitor in my office. We did this for a number of years and it was always entertaining to see what we were catching, and useful for evaluating how well the traps work. We often fished the traps several times a week, but we did not know how often the fish were coming into and going from the traps. It soon became evident that, depending on the species, this could be quite frequent. In one instance there was a small cunner or bergal in the trap and a larger cunner eyeing it from outside the trap. After a few minutes the larger fish came into the trap, attacked the smaller fish and left. All this occurred within about three seconds. Thus, we have to be careful how we interpret our trap catches because some of these fish which are used to orienting around structure can easily enter and leave these traps at will.

storms and low summer wind conditions, plus the development of an algae bloom, resulted in low dissolved oxygen and high sulfide over an area of 3,320 square miles of the ocean. There were extensive mortalities of bottom-dwelling organisms such as crabs, scallops, barnacles, starfish, worms and clams. Surf clams were the most documented, with an estimated mortality rate of 61.5% over an area of 2,600 square miles. Other marine animals such as eels and sea bass were also killed in large numbers. Another result was large numbers of summer flounder escaped the low oxygen levels by moving into estuaries, to the delight of recreational fishermen.

The area around RUMFS has seen two internationally recognized scientific and engineering advances since the American Revolution. The first was the development of the trans-Atlantic wireless with one of the terminals, an 853-foot tower, anchored in Mystic Islands. Concrete supports from the tower can still be seen scattered along Radio Road, and a part of the base of the tower lies in the front yard of the Tuckerton Historical Society. The second was the deployment in 1990 of a fiber optic cable from RUMFS to two spots about three miles out in the Atlantic Ocean. Built with the help of Woods Hole Oceanographic Institute, AT&T and New Jersey Bell Telephone Co., the fiber optic link provided continuous long-term measurements on the nearshore continental shelf outside Little Egg Inlet.

This long-term ecosystem observatory enabled Rutgers University scientists and their collaborators to detect changes in marine processes not possible with the "snapshot technology" provided by traditional oceanographic techniques. Specific objectives of the research program were to investigate nearshore bottom boundary layer conditions to improve physical models of hydrodynamic processes affecting sediment transport; examine sedimentary processes involved in sand ridge formation and nearshore sediment dynamics; determine processes affecting survival during late larval and early juvenile stages for economically important fish and invertebrates; and understand processes controlling bottom community structure.

Major findings of these far-reaching studies included extensive mapping, a better understand-

Fish sampling by RUMFS personnel in a patch of invasive Phragmites *at Hog Island in the Mullica River.*

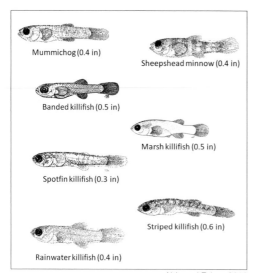

Able and Fahay, 2010

Above, left: Illustrations of representative juvenile killifishes (and their lengths) collected as part of RUMFS sampling. These species are the dominant group of intertidal fishes in marshes and creeks. Above, right: Pop nets deployed in RUMFS boat basin at night capture representative fish during all seasons.

ing of the dynamics of upwelling, of sediment and benthic invertebrate community dynamics, and of inner shelf habitat and dynamics for larval and juvenile fish.

Of perhaps singular importance was the realization of the rapidity of change in the nearshore ocean, a factor that was previously underappreciated and based only on small-scale, low-frequency observations. The numerous findings from these studies were communicated live to scientists and, perhaps more importantly, to the general public via the World Wide Web. In many ways the developments and sense of place at this observatory set the stage for the application of Autonomous Underwater Vehicles (AUVs), such as the Teledyne-Webb Research Slocum glider, for gathering data on the continental shelf off southern New Jersey and the first-ever crossing of the Atlantic by RU-27, an unmanned glider.

Otter trawls have been deployed from small boats to capture bottom fish in a variety of deeper habitats. Below: Image of fish in a trap at RUMFS boat basin as seen on a monitor at the station. This real-time camera system was designed to test trap effectiveness.

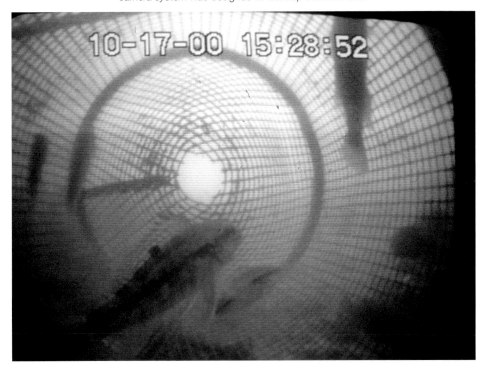

Epilogue

We don't understand our estuarine systems very well because they are the hidden part of the planet. They are underwater, a real disadvantage to us air-breathing humans. That obstacle, compounded by our lack of knowledge of basic natural history, confounds our ability to conserve and effectively manage estuarine resources.

At RUMFS, activities are continuing some of the same resource-based and ecological interests started by the Nelsons and other early researchers. We are trying to uncover the hidden parts of the planet with a variety of technological advances and the advantages of "place," the idea that we are uniquely located for this mission. We, and the Department of Marine and Coastal Sciences, are fostering better human activities in the sea. They include better diving techniques, the use of manned and unmanned submersibles, and other approaches such as fiber optic linkages to the inner continental shelf and the enhanced development of "acoustic video" that provides the ability to "see" in typically turbid estuaries.

The specific advantages of RUMFS as a "place" are numerous and varied. They begin with the long history, more than 125 years of research in the area, and continue in more recent years with the protection of the estuarine system by several agencies. Most importantly the large holdings in the Jacques Cousteau National Estuarine Research Reserve, approximately 115,000 acres, are protected as a result of multiple federal and state partners and the adjacent upstream activities of the Pinelands National Reserve. Together these make the Mullica River-Great Bay estuary the cleanest estuary in the Northeast and one of the cleanest along the East Coast. At the same time, the more impacted Barnegat Bay is providing a focus on estuarine restoration through the Barnegat Bay Partnership and its numerous allies. These contributions, plus the location of the station just inside the inlet to the Mullica River-Great Bay estuary and the southern entrance to Little Egg Harbor and Barnegat Bay, provide RUMFS investigators the ideal place for day-to-day as well as long-term observations of this hidden part of the planet.

When these advantages are married to the unique facilities of the former Station 119 at RUMFS, there is unlimited opportunity for research and hands-on teaching. The nature of these facilities makes it exceptionally appropriate as a research facility. There is, for instance, a railway for moving boats and research equipment into and out of the station. There's a cupola that provides exceptional visual access to much of the lower portion of both estuaries and the adjacent ocean. The former Station 119 cisterns that were once used to collect rainwater for fighting fires are now incorporated into the flow-through seawater system that provides holding and research facilities in several laboratories. The boat basin created by the Coast Guard, while often in need of dredging, provides access for RUMFS vessels of a variety of sizes and capabilities. The Station 119 porches provide for additional dining, meeting and sample sorting space under very pleasant conditions for much of the year.

The proximity of these and other newly renovated spaces to the uncontaminated fauna could not be better because the fish, crabs and other invertebrates can swim and crawl under the facilities at high tide. The advantages of this access cannot be overestimated because it provides for adaptive sampling in response to episodic events such as storms. The best example is when we once collected an adult winter flounder for tagging from the flooded Great Bay Boulevard. Other special sampling just a few feet from our offices and laboratories has included night-lighting for larval fish and lobsters for laboratory experiments, pop netting for pelagic fish, light-trap sampling for larval fish and tagging experiments on juvenile fish. The same proximity has provided for novel studies in our boat basin of the effects of dredging, which are applicable elsewhere.

One accepted metric for conducting successful science is the rate of publication in the peer-reviewed literature. However, evaluating this for place-based research is problematic because often the clearest contributions come from syntheses which are retrospective in nature and do not necessarily generate novel discoveries. Yet these contributions are often serendipitous. An excellent example is analysis of climate change. Many place-based time series collections began before this phenomenon was generally recognized, and these series are contributing uniquely to an improved understanding of this phenomenon. This is evident in our study area by the change in larval fish supply to estuaries and the response of Atlantic croaker, which have expanded to more northern waters, such as in New Jersey, to the point they are the basis for commercial and recreational fisheries.

The same advantages of "place" to research also serve to foster excellent teaching opportunities, and this is especially true at RUMFS and in the Jacques Cousteau National Estuarine Research Reserve. At RUMFS, the proximity to natural habitats at all hours of the day and night, through all seasons, brings the natural history of the estuary to both undergraduate and graduate classes and students, postdocs and resident and visiting faculty in a way that they may not have previously experienced. Formal training is constantly occurring and has included over fifty graduate students and twenty-three postdocs. While formal classroom training is the order of business at any university facility, at RUMFS there is a largely unrecognized informal education that occurs as well, as technicians, visiting scientists, reserve managers and the public have the opportunity to observe the basics of life in the estuary. One of these occasions is the annual "Open House", which every year provides 300 to 800 people of all ages the opportunity to understand these unique facilities and the estuary as a whole. Because the station is embedded in the Jacques Cousteau Reserve, the overlap offers other opportunities for learning.

Another of these opportunities is the Research Internships in Ocean Sciences (RIOS) program in which summer interns, supported by the National Science Foundation-Research Experiences for Undergraduates program, spend ten weeks conducting research mentored by RUMFS personnel. Others use the station

Camera crew in salt marsh at RUMFS recording JCNERR education segment.

for day- to week-long long field trips from all Rutgers campuses as well as from other colleges and universities. Besides these varied teaching activities, there are numerous recent undergraduates who as technicians receive training for future job possibilities. Since 1989, numerous technicians have received this kind of experience. Occasionally these kinds of opportunities are extended to New Jersey high school students. Notable examples include students from the Marine Academy of Science and Technology (MAST) in Highlands, and the Marine Academy of Technology and Environmental Science (MATES) in Manahawkin.

So, as of this writing, the long and storied history of Station 119 continues on. It has seen many changes of face and purpose. Though it is no longer in the business of saving lives, it is involved in saving something just as important. And in the process, it's serving not only science and the planet, but also the many individuals whose sense of excitement and quest for answers have been inspired by this singular place.

The Rutgers University Invertebrate Identification class on a winter outing aboard the R.V. Arabella with instructors Fred Grassle (upper left) and Rose Petrecca (third from left). Below: A typical group of RUMFS summer personnel includes faculty, postdocs, staff, graduate students, summer interns and technicians.

RUMFS (both)

119

Individuals involved in acoustic tracking of fish to determine habitat use patterns in the Mullica River-Great Bay estuary during the 1990s – early 2000s, from left to right; Stacy Hagan, Mark Sullivan, Claire Ng, Dana Sackett, Ken Able and, (front) Tom Grothues. Below: Harbor seals from nearby winter colony hauled out on the floating docks at RUMFS.

Acknowledgements

Over the last two decades many people helped to fill in the holes in the road, the wood causeway, and the gaps in this history. Many also recounted aspects of No. 119's history as a Coast Guard station; Dick Handschuch, John Hedgepeth and John Connery, former residents, provided insights into the day-to-day life of Coast Guard activities; Wick York and Tim Dring were especially helpful with references and information based on their extensive experience with Coast Guard stations and their history; Tim also provides perspective in the Introduction. Other details of the Coast Guard days were supplied by the National Archives in New York City and in Washington D.C., especially Mark Mollan at the latter. Joe Dobarro, early on, pointed out the value of these collections.

Others filled in the history of this facility when it was part of Rutgers University. Among these were Dr. Norbert Psuty, who shared details and photographs before and during the earliest days of RUMFS; Deborah Whitcraft (Museum of New Jersey Maritime History); Bill Kane, and Jeannette Lloyd who assisted with older references and photographs. Kent Mountford lent his expertise to the Foreword as well as editorial comments. Stewart Farrell shared his experience while he was using the abandoned building as a base of organization for research. Melbourne Carriker shared his photos and details of the operation of the barge *Cynthia*. Walt Canzonier recalled the activities of the New Jersey Agricultural Experiment Station in Great Bay–Little Egg Harbor in the early days. Paul Hamer and Bill Figley provided photographs depicting research activities by New Jersey Department of Environmental Protection.

The Ocean County Library, and especially Colleen Goode, assisted with access to early newspaper articles. The Tuckerton Historical Society was helpful in providing details of local history, especially Pete Stemmer and Barbara Bolton. The Ocean County Historical Society assisted with other early records. The JCNERR manager (Mike De Luca) and staff (Mike Kennish, Lisa Auermuller, Melanie Reding, Gregg Sakowicz, and Kim Capone) have supported RUMFS activities in a variety of ways that helped to uncover this history. Photos of early days at RUMFS came from the collections of Polly Durand, Kevin Schick, Bob Christian, Royal Nadeau, Richard Coffman, and Roger Hoden. Former students Dave and Donna Vaughan, Kevin Shickand and Joe Arsenault shared their experiences in the early days of RUMFS. Rose Petrecca supplied background information on the history of the larger research vessels. Details of Superstorm Sandy came from David Robinson from the Office of the New Jersey State Climatologist and from Gregg Sakowicz. Photos related to Sandy were made available by Gina Petruzzelli. Jenna Rackovan helped to organize the numerous image files. Word processing and editorial expertise were provided by Carol Van Pelt. Sue, Nathan, and Peter Able edited the first complete draft and offered suggestions along the way. Others who assisted in ideas and editing include Judy Grassle and Colin Able. Down The Shore Publishing was central to bringing this book to fruition; Ray Fisk saw the value of this history and provided the context for its publication. Steve Warren made my stilted scientific writing much more readable. Leslee Ganss designed the book and organized the numerous photos into an effective final product. I am grateful to all of the above.

The author was fortunate to be part of the Rutgers University Center for Coastal and Environmental Studies and its successor, the Institute of Marine and Coastal Sciences, during much of the history of RUMFS.

During RUMFS Annual Intern Olympics, causeway bowling (above) is a typical activity, rain or shine; tug of war (below) takes place over a marsh pool,with staff (far side) vs. interns (near side).

SELECT BIBLIOGRAPHY

Able, Kenneth W., and Fahay, Michael P. *The First Year in the Life of Estuarine Fishes in the Middle Atlantic Bight*. Rutgers University Press, New Brunswick, N.J. 1998.

_____ *Ecology of Estuarine Fishes: Temperate Waters of the Western North Atlantic*. Johns Hopkins University Press, Baltimore, Md. 2010.

Burger, Joanna. *A Naturalist Along the Jersey Shore*. Rutgers University Press, New Brunswick, N.J. 1996.

Forman, Richard T. T. *Pine Barrens: Ecosystem and Landscapes*. Academic Press, New York, N.Y. 1979.

Kennedy, Victor S.; Newell, Rodger I. E., and Eble, Albert F., *The Eastern Oyster:* Crassostrea virginica. Maryland Sea Grant, College Park, Md. 1996.

Kennish, Michael J., and Lutz, Rich A. *Ecology of Barnegat Bay, New Jersey*. Springer, New York, N.Y. 1984.

Lloyd, John Bailey. *Two Centuries of History on Long Beach Island*. Down The Shore Publishing, West Creek, N.J. 2005.

Mazzella, Scott. *Surviving Sandy: Long Beach Island and the Greatest Storm of the Jersey Shore*. Down The Shore Publishing, West Creek, N.J. 2013.

Mountford, Kent. *Closed Sea: From the Manasquan to the Mullica, a History of Barnegat Bay*. Down The Shore Publishing, West Creek, N.J. 2002.

Savadove, Larry, and Buchholz, Margaret Thomas. *Great Storms of the Jersey Shore*. Down The Shore Publishing and *The Sandpaper,* Inc., co-publishers, West Creek, N.J. 1993.

Shanks, Ralph; York, Wick; and Shanks, Lisa Woo. (ed.) *U. S. Life-saving Service: Heroes, Rescues and Architecture of the Early Coast Guard*. Castaño Books, Petaluma, Ca. 1996.

Veasey, David. *Guarding New Jersey's Shore—Lighthouses and Life-Saving Stations*. Arcadia Publishing, Charleston, S.C. 2000.

Woodward, Carl R., and Waller, Ingrid N. *New Jersey's Agricultural Experiment Station 1880-1930*. New Jersey Agricultural Experiment Station, New Brunswick, N.J. 1932.

INDEX

ABOUT THE AUTHOR

Ken Able is a Distinguished Professor in the Department of Marine and Coastal Sciences, and is Director of the Marine Field Station at Rutgers University. His diverse interests include estuarine ecosystems with a focus on life history and the ecology of fishes with an emphasis on habitat quality. The history, both natural and human, of field stations — and their role in the progress of science — continues to intrigue the author.

http://marine.rutgers.edu/rumfs

If you enjoyed this book you may also be interested in:

Closed Sea: From the Manasquan to the Mullica, A History of Barnegat Bay
by Kent Mountford ISBN 1-59322-027-8

Golden Light: The 1878 Diary of Captain Thomas Rose Lake
by James B. Kirk II ISBN 0-945582-85-4

Eighteen Miles of History on Long Beach Island
by John Bailey Lloyd ISBN 0945582-17-X

Six Miles at Sea: A Pictorial History of Long Beach Island
by John Bailey Lloyd ISBN 0-945582-03-X

Down The Shore Publishing specializes in books, calendars, cards and videos about the Jersey Shore and coastal interests. For a free catalog of all our titles or to be included on our mailing list, just send us a request:

Down The Shore Publishing
Box 100, West Creek, NJ 08092

info@down-the-shore.com
www.down-the-shore.com